Abraham

A Novel

UNBEARABLE BOOKS / AUTONOMEDIA

UB–1: *Spermatagonia: The Isle of Man,* bart plantenga
UB–2: *Negativeland,* Doug Nufer
UB–3: *Neo Phobe,* Jim Feast with Ron Kolm
UB–4: *Shorts Are Wrong,* Mike Topp
UB–5: *The Hotel of Irrevocable Acts,* Carl Watson
UB–6: *The Ass's Tale,* John Farris
UB–7: *This Young Girl Passing,* Donald Breckenridge
UB–8: *Love Does Not Make Me Gentle or Kind,* Chavisa Woods
UB–9: *A Superintendent's Eyes,* Steve Dalachinsky
UB–10: *Kali's Day,* Bonny Finberg
UB–11: *The Rat Hunt Boys,* Anna Mockler
UB–12: *The Beer Mystic,* bart plantenga
UB–13: *Night Shift,* Ron Kolm
UB–14: *Pareidolia,* Carl Watson
UB–15: *Long Day, Counting Tomorrow,*
Jim Feast with Carol Wierzbicki
UB–16: *Flasher,* Tsaurah Litzky
UB–17: *Welcome Distractions,* Carol Wierzbicki
UB–18: *Abraham,* Sparrow
UB–19: *Among the Boat People,* Nhi Manh Chung
UB–20: *Welcome to the Barbecue,* Ron Kolm
UB–21: *A Foreigner in Hades,* Philip Rostek

Abraham

A Novel

Sparrow

Autonomedia

Unbearable Books are published and distributed by
Autonomedia
POB 568 Williamsburgh Station
Brooklyn NY 11211–0568 USA
www.autonomedia.org
info@autonomedia.org

For Violet and Sylvia

Abraham: A Novel

INTRODUCTION

This book is the diary of Robert Klassen, a chiropractor in Stone Ridge, New York. It covers a little more than a year (2010–2011). Klassen's note follows.

AUTHOR'S NOTE

Let me explain my chronological notation. Each month is encoded as a letter, with "A" for January, "B" for February, etc.; preceding the letter is the day of the month. So "1:C" equals March 1. The second notation for the day, if there is one, is the time. "p" stands for PM. I remove the colon from the time, so 4:51 PM is notated as *451p*.

1:C

I'm studying the Mexican War. It's remarkable that thundering battles took place in little California towns now filled with aging hippies, surfers, and rich software consultants. I'm thinking of the Battle of Monterey.

Commodore Robert F. Stockton seized Los Angeles with 50 Marines on August 13, 1846.

451p
My son has begun saying the word "panim" (with the accent on the second syllable). He says it constantly, with a teasing look in his eye. I'm trying to guess what "panim" means.

2:C

All history buffs have a period they wish they had lived in. For me, it's the 6th century BCE in Etruria.

421p
"What would you like for dinner?" I asked Grange today.
"Panim!"

456p
A number of American soldiers deserted and joined the enemy, early in the Mexican War. "Many were Irish Catholic immigrants who sympathized with the Mexicans because of their shared faith and felt themselves religiously persecuted in the predominantly Protestant U.S. Army," writes Martin Dugard in *The Training Ground: Grant, Lee, Sherman, and Davis in the Mexican War, 1846–1848*.

601p
Research is essential to historians. Just as an artist painting a landscape must study its shadows precisely, a historian must examine archives. Even in his sleep, a researcher must work.

Last night, in a dream, I studied rare Spanish documents from the Mexican War. Although I cannot read Spanish, in my dream I was fluent.

3:C

Grange and I traveled to the mall to buy raisins and figs. There we saw a man with a noticeable limp. He was about 40, and wore blue pants. He walked as if there was a potato in his shoe.

357p

The seeds of the Civil War are present in the Mexican War: Robert E. Lee proves himself a brilliant officer, while Abraham Lincoln, as an Illinois Congressman, argues against the invasion.

4:C

My son had a high fever, and grew frightened. He stared into my eyes with terror.

"You will be fine," I told him. "You'll be better than ever. You'll be as lively as a Chinese circus."

And I believed what I said — almost completely.

604p

"Sit on the table with me," my wife asked. So I did, though we'd never done that before — sat together on the kitchen table. Winnie wanted to cry.

"I get so worried when Grange is ill," she said, within her tears. "I don't want to lose him."

I cradled Winnie, gazing at a bowl of pears. She'd set three Bosc pears in the bowl yesterday, and they were ripening.

5:C

People are always surprised to discover that I'm married to an African-American woman. I don't seem "hip" enough for that. But they don't realize Black people are no more hip than Eskimos or Germans. They just seem mysterious to whites because of slavery.

For hundreds of years, white people wondered: "What are the slaves thinking, in their shacks? Are they preparing a revolt, or performing voodoo?" Well, they probably *were* preparing a revolt and performing voodoo — also praying to Jesus, and just complaining. After the Great Migration north after World War I, white anxiety took a new form. Now they viewed African-Americans as "hip" — inventing new art forms.

350p
I found this quote in Ralph Waldo Emerson's journal from October, 1862:

> George Francis Train said in a public speech in New York, "Slavery is a divine institution." "So is hell," exclaimed an old man in the crowd.

437p
Yesterday it snowed, and today the "aftersnow" is falling — the snow that collected on branches, now dislodged by the wind. Aftersnow is larger than snow; it's made of clumps, which fall with majestic slowness.

3:L

I'm glad I was never circumcised. This decision was unusual in 1969, when I was born, but my mother had read *Circumcision Exposed: Rethinking a Medical and Cultural Tradition* by Billy Ray Boyd. She was an early "intactivist" — that's the term for opponents of foreskin-removal. (I once heard her tell her friend Clara: "Do you realize circumcision was first instituted to prevent masturbation?")

421p
Grange is healthy again.

7:C

One of the pleasures of married life is lying with my wife in bed, once our child is asleep, chatting. Today Winnie told me this joke, which she heard at work:

> "What's red and invisible? No tomatoes."
> She laughed afterwards, in her quiet, almost hiccuping manner.
> Social workers tell strange jokes.

507p

The U. S. could have annexed all of Mexico after General Winfield Scott captured Mexico City in 1847. The main arguments against annexation were racist. "Ours is a government of the white man," John C. Calhoun decreed in Congress. Besides, the Mexicans refused to be enslaved. One goal of the war was to increase the number of slave states.

8:C

"Where would you like to walk today?" I asked Grange.
"Panim!"
He's learning that secret words can make you stronger than your father.

9:C

Bathing is important when you're a chiropractor. Patients have an extremely acute sense of smell.

406p

Grange and I went for a walk, and he noticed a small card lying on the road. He ran up to it, looked at me for permission, and when I nodded, picked it up. On it was a quote from Edith Wharton:

> If only we'd stop trying to be happy we'd have a pretty
> good time.

I gazed at this message — which apparently fell from a "direct mail" envelope. Then we walked back home, past the stream with little globules of ice along the edge, like glass beads.
Back at home, we measured the Edith Wharton card with a ruler. It's exactly 3" by 4 5/8".

406p

For some reason, I can't forget the anecdote of Robert E. Lee receiving a letter from his wife during the Mexican War and opening it with a bayonet.

10: C

I heard an airplane tonight, as I lay in bed with Winnie. Our house is so remote that the sound of an airplane is quite unusual. It's been two years since I've heard a motor up above.

11:C

Grange and I stood outside during a blizzard. The snow was wet and thick. After a time, a branch deep in the woods fell off a tree. We saw it collapse and crash. At that exact moment, a churchbell rang.

Grange and I turned to each other, smiling.

355p

I awoke today with a whistle in my nose. Do you know what I mean? Sometimes your nose is slightly congested, so when you breathe, it whistles. You become an inadvertent flautist.

607p

I've been listening to Billie Holiday recently. The song "They Can't Take That Away from Me" is stuck in my mind:

> The way your smile just beams,
> The way you sing off key,
> The way you haunt my dreams;
> No, no! They can't take that away from me!

But I keep remembering the line wrong. I sing to myself:

> The way you dance off key.

And some people *do* dance off key!

751p

The "roof" of the mouth is misnamed. A roof is the outside of a building, not the inside. The term should be "ceiling" of the mouth.

12:C

Grange and I went for a walk. Yesterday it rained, but today it was cold, so all the puddles had turned into fragile ice. Grange leapt on the ice, breaking it. The puddle-ice was so thin it not only cracked, but made a satisfying smashing sound, as if it were glass.

Grange went up and down the road, methodically breaking every patch of ice. The one-time 4-year-olds are methodical while destroying puddle-ice.

13:C

Today I again had the "whistle" in my nose when I awoke. But it was a higher note; I'd say a C sharp.

342p

Never in history were two opposing figures so well-cast as Robert E. Lee and Abraham Lincoln. Lee was aloof, courtly, genteel — he epitomized the Southern aristocracy. Lincoln was his opposite: gangly, melancholy, born to physical labor. Lincoln was American capitalism embodied, where anyone with sufficient ambition, intelligence and (especially) luck, can rise to the very heights.

I once visited Lee's grave at Washington and Lee University in Lexington, Virginia — supposedly the only recumbent statue in the United States. Robert E. Lee's marble body lies on the ground, his head resting on an elbow, a womanly pose.

14:C

Last night I was about to go to sleep when I smelled a gaseous odor outside the bedroom. At first I assumed my wife or my son, or both, were farting. I checked the stove, to see if the gas was on. No.

Then I remembered we have propane heat. Perhaps the propane was leaking. Could the house explode at any moment? Or would we be gassed in our sleep like the Jews in Auschwitz, with Zyklon B?

But what could I do? Wake everyone up and drive to a motel? All because of a vague suspicion? I lay in bed, offered my life to the Sovereign Divine, and somehow fell asleep.

In my dream, Winnie and I were walking in New York City. We came to a free amusement arcade, which one could enter from the sidewalk. "Let's go in!" she said, gaily. The interior resembled a low-rent theme park. Women in 1920s-style outfits danced on a stage. Barkers barked. Betting wheels spun. We both loved the festive air.

Just before you exited, you mounted a low stage where a man in a boater hat offered little presents. We each received a small white napkin, formed into a ball — and inside each was a live chick! I could hear the little bird peeping.

I awoke.

417p
Today my wife explained that the smell is a dead animal in the walls.

15:C

Grange's word "panim" has evolved into "paniom."

642p
The smell is deeper, richer. Clearly it's not mere gas. It's rotting mouse-flesh. (Mole-flesh?) The stench is strongest in the guest room — so strong it's almost a taste.

"For the next few weeks, we can only invite guests who have no sense of smell," Winnie advised.

16:C

The smell is now halfway between that of frying sausages and shit. It can't be just a little mouse. It must be a larger creature, perhaps even a gopher, who sneaked into our walls — and got terrifyingly trapped, like a character in an Edgar Allan Poe story.

417p
Columbus made five voyages to the New World, and never once stepped onto American soil. He confined himself to islands: Hispaniola, Cuba, the Bahamas, Jamaica. It's almost as if some mystical force prevented him from reaching our continent. Or was he just too lazy to travel the extra 49 miles?

601p
It was another day of puddle-breaking for me and Grange. (I include myself because I broke two.) The most fun is to break a puddle with water underneath – which makes a satisfying *crik-sloosh*.

17:C

Today the smell is much more like a homeless person — like having an invisible hobo staying in your house.

But the good news is my friend Arthur, the biology teacher, tells me the smell will dissipate soon. "That's the beauty of putrefaction," Arthur observed, ironically.

641p
From age 10 till 12, I avidly collected stamps. My favorite country was Burma, though I only had five Burmese stamps. Two of the stamps depicted tiny golden temples.

18:C

The smell is beginning to dissipate, just as Arthur predicted. The bacteria have eaten through most of the gopher, or whatever mammal it was. (It could not have been a reptile. That richly horrifying smell was distinctly mammalian.)

In a second conversation, Arthur said: "Remember, we think of this process as decay, but a more appropriate word would be 'digestion.' It stinks for the same reason flatulence stinks."

19:C

Winnie explained the subprime housing crisis to me. "It's as if one of our neighbors gave an open house, and invited everyone on the street," she said. "And at the end, they handed out free cookies: 'Here, take some cookies! I want you to have these!' And they loaded each person down with 15 or 16 cookies. Then, six months later, they called everyone up and said, 'By the way, each of those cookies cost $1200.' And we then discover that when we signed their guestbook, we unknowingly entered a contract — perfectly legally binding — to pay $1200 for each cookie. And if we don't have the money, we lose our homes.

"Eventually, enough people can't pay the $1200 per cookie, and the swindlers go broke. At this point, the government gives them free subsidies — because they're 'too big to fail.'"

359p
Now I can walk into our bedroom and not even notice the stench.

629p
The early history of submarines is laughable. For one thing, the first American one was called the "Turtle." David Bushnell built it in 1776 to attack British warships, and in the early morning of September 7, he did assault one, in New York Harbor. But the ship — probably the HMS Eagle — had too strong a hull. Bushnell (the entire crew of the submarine) couldn't drill through it, to attach a 150 pound keg of gunpowder. Disoriented, the Turtle drifted away.

642p
Yesterday it snowed, and this morning a few snowflakes are still gliding aimlessly through my backyard. For some reason, I imagine snowflakes speaking Italian.
"Where are you going?" I ask a snowflake.
"Cerco mia madre*," she replies.

653p
Thinking of the history of America, there are so many invasions: the attempted conquest of Canada in 1812, the Mexican War, the Spanish-American War, the long struggle in the Philippines, Vietnam, the Dominican Republic, Grenada, Iraq. In fact, America began as a Colonial influx, from England, France and Spain.
America is one long invasion.

21:C

Lately when Grange breaks a puddle, he slides on it first, shouting, "Zoooooooey!"

*" I search for my mother."

412p

Abraham Lincoln, I just learned, trimmed his beard. I never thought of that. I just assumed his beard grew only on his chin. In fact, for a short time Abraham had a full beard, then reconsidered. Ultimately, Lincoln had an "artist's beard" — that's what it was called at the time.

A photograph of him taken with that early, overgrown beard became popular in Europe, and was depicted in engravings in France, Germany and Hungary. (This is from *Our Lincoln: New Perspectives on Lincoln and His World*, edited by Eric Foner.)

22:C

I awoke with a start today. My right eyelid had twisted in the night, and my eye was tearing. In the confusion of my dream — I worked in a bookstore — my eyelid must have become tangled.

716p

My wife is in a jolly mood lately, because the Stock Market is crashing. "These might be the death throes of the money-system," Winnie said today.

23:C

I'm still reading *Our Lincoln*. It's one of the bicentennial books celebrating the 200th anniversary of Abe's birth. Here is a surprising thought:

> Abraham Lincoln, whose command of the English language surpassed that of nearly every other American president, did not produce a book during his lifetime (unless one counts the manuscript denying the divinity of the Bible that according to local lore, he wrote in New Salem, Illinois, in the 1830s and then destroyed at the urging of friends).

Lincoln didn't write books for two reasons: 1) He thought in short bursts. 2) His writing was intended for immediate political effect. Lincoln's compositions were closer to journalism — his monumental piece was an occasional work, for the Battle of Gettysburg.

24:C

Do you know those thin rubber pads one uses to open difficult jars? Today I saw Winnie holding ours. (It's red, with the name of a local insurance company on it: "Brainford Insurance.") My wife was opening a bottle of peach juice. What surprised me was that she poured water on the pad before she used it. "It only works if you add water," Winnie explained. What a curious belief!

221p
Maybe the best essay in *Our Lincoln* is about his conscious use of symbology to create his persona ("Visualizing Lincoln: Abraham Lincoln as Student, Subject and Patron of the Visual Arts"). Abraham was obsessed with images of George Washington. Harold Holzer tells the story:

> We know that Lincoln understood the emotional power of these domestic icons if only through one of his funny stories about the response evoked by one crudely displayed Washington likeness. It seemed that an American living in England had grown weary of Englishmen deriding America's greatest hero, so in response he hung a picture of the first president in his host's privy. In Lincoln's view, this seemingly irreverent gesture was in fact "very appropriate... for their [sic] Is Nothing that Will Make an Englishman Shit so quick as the Sight of Genl Washington."

I *suspected* Lincoln was secretly profane! I want to read a vast collection of his dirty jokes!

25:C

My family went driving today, and came upon the town of New Owen. We got out to inspect the village. New Owen is small, with no more than three streets, but it is the most symmetric town I have ever seen. If there is a mailbox on one end of Main Street, there will certainly be a mailbox in the analogous spot on the other end. Right in the middle of town is a white Methodist Church, which itself is perfectly symmetrical.

I began to wonder if pairs of twins live in New Owen, one on each side of town, in houses that are mirror images of one another.

336p
From Catherine Clinton's essay in *Our Lincoln*:

> [Abraham and Mary] often read poetry aloud to each other, and both penned verses. Lincoln's compositions occasionally appeared (unsigned) in the local paper. Lincoln's sentimental visit to his childhood home, he said, "aroused feelings in me which were certainly poetry."

Lincoln was a poet! I should have known. The only way to produce great prose is to write hundreds of crappy verses. Which he published in the newspaper, anonymously — just like Walt Whitman. Maybe every writer of the 19th century anonymously published in the daily papers. Did Thoreau? Did Emerson?

26:C

Here's a surprise — Lincoln had no charisma:

> For their part, thousands of Union clergy saw in Lincoln a president who warranted respect, even admiration, not simply ex officio but because they found in him qualities to be extolled. His was not charismatic power, properly understood, and there was no personal cult of Lincoln.

426p
I brought Grange to the Easter Parade in Kingston, then we walked around a little. We climbed Abeel Street, past two or three Victorian houses ample as Dutch schooners. The sidewalk, for half a block, was littered with broken slate. We had to walk in the street.

Some cities exist only due to inertia. Their economic raison d'être is over, but they can't be erased, like a bad drawing. They continue, in a sullen, lost way.

607p
I'm listening to *Blonde on Blonde* by Dylan. I have always loved the line (from "Can You Please Crawl Out Your Window?"):

> If he needs a third eye he just grows one.

But who is "he"? Dylan mumbles the song, so it's not easy to know. I'll look up the lyrics on the Internet.

614p
Well, the "he" is never specific — although clearly Dylan is attempting to seduce some woman attached to that "he." Here's the whole verse:

> He looks so truthful; is this how he feels?
> Trying to peel the moon and expose it;
> With his businesslike anger and his bloodhounds that kneel.
> If he needs a third eye he just grows it.
> He just needs you to talk or to hand him his chalk,
> Or pick it up after he throws it.

I heard the line slightly wrong, but I had the concept right. Like all of Dylan's greatest lines, it's a sneering insult.

431p
Gradually puddle-smashing has evolved into a dance, for Grange – a little like an Irish jig.

27:C

Today the tongue fell out of my shoe. This is the first time that's ever happened to me. It was one of my brown Florsheims, which I've had for six years. I just pulled gently on the tongue, and out it came.

712p
In 2007 the first complete British history of the War of 1812 was written. The title is *1812: War with America* by Jon Latimer, published by Harvard University Press. That's how unimportant our nation is to England, that it took them 195 years to publish this book.

30:C

Today the snow has finally melted, and I can see my lawn for the first time since last November. The grass looks stunned and disoriented — like the face of a man who's just cut off his beard.

I guess snow *is* a beard — a white beard, in fact. (And many men grow beards in the winter, unconsciously emulating the earth.)

419p
History is an escape for me. Just as middle-aged women read romance novels, I read histories of Babylonia, to forget my life.

1:D

Today I was visiting my friend Arthur, and found three M&Ms on the floor of his living room. Two were blue; one was green. Without their companions, the candies looked extraterrestrial, like buttons from the console of a UFO.

406p
My wife found this quote in a book:

> "If you want to know what God thinks of money, just look
> at the people he gave it to." — Dorothy Parker

2:D

I love to read about ice harvesting in the Hudson Valley, how hundreds of workers — mostly men — would stand on frozen rivers and ponds, chop up the surface, haul it out, store it in ice houses. A thousand people worked daily on the Hudson River, earning between one and two dollars a day. Horses would fall through the ice and die. All from the human lust for ice water!

Arthur showed me an issue of the *Shawangunk Journal* with an article by A. J. Schenkman entitled "They Thirst for Ice, Part II." He points out that major hotels like the Astor House in New York City "knew that pure ice was essential for ice water and ice cream because ice's purity affected the taste of water and many desserts. Even butter churners demanded the purest quality ice when they needed to harden their butter so as not to affect its taste and quality." This was before refrigerators were available in the 1920s.

Probably ice *did* taste better then! We mock the connoisseurship of frozen water, but if we could taste their ice cream, we'd repent our ridicule.

3:D

There is, in the silence between husband and wife, a great melancholy hum. Winnie and I shared such a silence today, as Grange slept.

603p
My ancestors, on my father's side, kept slaves. And Winnie's ancestors, of course, were slaves. There is a tiny chance that my great-great-grandfather owned her great-great-grandfather — but I've never discussed this with her. How could I?

4:D

I saw my first robin of spring today. When I pointed him out to Winnie, she said: "Robins have been around for a couple weeks." My wife is much more alert to bird life than I.

417p
Today, while eating an apple, the stem went briefly up my nose. How humiliating!

5:D

I thought my wife was writing to Thomas Merton today. I saw a letter on the stand in the vestibule which she'd written, and I thought the addressee was Merton. But I'd read wrong: it was really Thomas Martin.

I could imagine Winnie and Merton having a fruitful correspondence. Both are serious, open-minded people. It's tragic that one cannot exchange letters with the dead.

Here's an idea: Thomas Merton impersonators. You pay a certain price to write a letter to Merton, or George Bernard Shaw, or Adolf Hitler, and a knowledgeable writer replies, in the persona of the deceased personality. Many people would pay to correspond with the dead.

6:D

One of my favorite names is Joyann. I met a woman with this name at the golf course two years ago, and I still see her occasionally. Her name was going to be just "Joy Ann," but her mother impulsively combined them into one word.

"Have you ever met another Joyann?" I asked.

"No," Joyann replied.

456p

I got a splinter underneath my fingernail (my right forefinger). I was reaching into a shelf and grazed the wood. It's not very painful, but it's disturbing to have a tiny invading spike.

I asked Winnie, and she poked a needle under my fingernail, but couldn't quite extract all of it — only 3/5 of the splinter.

7:D

On our walk, Grange discovered a CD — just the CD itself, with no packaging — lying on the road. Some guy must have flung it out of his car. Grange was delighted with his find, so we kept it.

Now I'm examining the artifact. You can learn so much just from the titles of songs! The band is The Jayhawks, the album "Rainy Day Music." I assume they're a country group, because one of their songs is "Tampa to Tulsa," and two have rural women's names in them: "Eyes of Sarahjane" and "Angelyne." Another song refers to the Christian religion: "Will I See You in Heaven" [with no question mark]. The record was made in 2003, released by "american recordings" [uncapitalized]. Strangely, the symbol of this company is an upside-down American flag. Is this logo a critique of our nation? Is the record company suggesting that America is topsy-turvy?

631p

My friend Lydia told me about a secret project called "the Montauk Experiment." She was shocked I hadn't heard of it. The Montauk Experiment is part of some vast conspiracy theory, but she wouldn't elaborate.

8:D

Today I was putting on a turtleneck shirt when I saw something in the sleeve. It was blue, and balled up — my wife's panties!

Winnie's underwear had nested in my shirt's arm.

357p

Arthur told me about The Jayhawks. "Basically, they were a rock band, but over time they got more country. The one you have, *Rainy Day Music*, is almost acoustic." Perhaps the person who threw the CD on the road (most likely a young man) disliked this acoustic version of The Jayhawks. (Of course, I'm not certain the CD was hurled out of a car. It might have fallen out by mistake. Or a 5 year old might've thrown it. Or an angry girlfriend. Roadside trash is full of uncertainties.)

9:D

I took the bus to New Paltz, and a stocky young woman with tattoos on her legs sat in the seat opposite me. When I looked up a few minutes later, she was cradling a rabbit.

"Is it a boy or a girl?" I asked her.

"A boy," she smiled.

"What's his name?"

"Rufus."

"He's bus-trained?"

"Yes."

"How old is he?"

"Four months!"

The rabbit was brown and compact, with soft fur. As his owner petted him, his eyes shined with gratitude. "I could have belonged to anyone, but God gave me to her," he was thinking.

"You keep him in your house?" I asked.

"Yes."

"But doesn't he chew your telephone wires?"

She smiled. "He used to, but he doesn't anymore."

"You taught him not to?"

"Yes."

Clearly my neighbor on the bus was a "rabbit-whisperer."

356p
I listened to "Angelyne" from the Jayhawks record, a wintry song of regret:

> Angelyne, forgive me;
> we threw it all away.
> You could never stand
> living with a man
> who could only lead you
> halfway to love.

I would call the music "fake Country"; it sounds more like Simon & Garfunkel than George Jones.

841p
Tonight I was reading *One Fish, Two Fish, Red Fish, Blue Fish* to Grange. I pointed at a red fish and asked, "What's his name?"
"Paniom!" Grange answered.

11:D

Just as a cop has a "beat," Grange and I have our beat. We walk a certain segment of our road, up to Swan Road, and in the other direction down to a neighbor's pond. On our circuit we notice how high the streams are, how large the mullein has grown. An oak was struck by lightning, and half of it fell over dramatically — we always pause there.

We keep our eyes open, patrolling our territory.

416p
The Montauk Project was conducted at Camp Hero on Montauk, Long Island from the late 60s until the 80s. Its purpose was to develop psychic powers, such as materializing objects out of thin air, teleportation, and time travel. Eventually, the researchers created a stable "Time Tunnel." Most of these allegations were made by Preston Nichols, who "regained the blanked memories of his role as chief technician for the project only after years of struggle." According to Nichols: "No one has picked up a tangible future beyond 2012 AD. There is a very abrupt wall there with nothing on the other side."

452p

Two weeks ago, my wife bought a 5 pound bag of potatoes, and when the potatoes ran out, I was about to throw away the bag when I noticed its design: a cartoony drawing of three potatoes (which are actually labeled "POTATOES"). Behind them is a green field (labeled "COLORADO"), beyond that snow-capped peaks. Beneath the whole drawing is written "Quality As High As Our Mountains." The bag comes from White Mountain Farm in Mosca, Colorado. I folded up the bag, and now it's in a drawer of my desk. Sometimes I unfold it and admire the art, with its three bold colors. (The mountains are blue beneath their snow.) It's a kind of folk commercial art — the potatoes larger than the Rocky Mountains.

12:D

The trees are growing leaves at amazing speed. Are they this quick every spring? I can't remember. They're producing the foliage in just two or three days — and it's been a dry month!

13:D

Today, after work, I stopped in at Olive's Café on an impulse. It's a little dining room in the back of a convenience store in the Shokan shopping mall. Olive's is a homespun place, with comfortable chairs, green oilskin tablecloths. You overhear conversations of working men and women.

And no one wipes the tables! I beheld the constellation of crumbs in front of me. Also on my table was the receipt for a bus ticket from Adirondack Trailways. I examined it carefully. In this Age of Surveillance, a bus ticket tells a lot. A person named Reese traveled from Kingston to New York City. She or he purchased the ticket on 04/23/10 at 2:43 p.m., using Bankcard 2556. The transaction was conducted by "Agent 37."

Drinking my chamomile tea, I pictured Reese, a 26 year old guy with slick black hair.

15:D

I'm reading James M. McPherson's short life of Abraham Lincoln. The whole book is only 65 pages; it's a historian's version of a haiku. *Abraham Lincoln* is a spiritual metaphor, like *Siddhartha* by Hermann Hesse. (But

Lincoln's life is the opposite of Buddha's, come to think of it. He began in a contemplative forest, and ended a Prince.) In a short book, the basic rudiments of Lincoln's life are clearly visible: his parents' illiteracy, his father's bullying. Lincoln became a thinker because his mother died of "milk sick" — probably the result of cows eating poisonous white snakeroot — and his stepmother, Sarah Bush Johnston, could read, encouraging Abraham's intellectual talents with *Pilgrim's Progress* and the King James Bible.

McPherson pens this telling passage:

> The teenaged Abraham's thinly veiled disdain for the life of a backwards farmer doubtless irritated his father. Abraham in turn resented the requirement of law and custom that any wages he earned before he reached the age of twenty-one — by hiring out to neighbors to split rails, for example — must be turned over to his father. Abraham Lincoln's hatred of slavery, which denied to slaves the "fruits of their labor," may have been influenced by Thomas Lincoln's expropriation of Abraham's earnings.

Lincoln had empathy for slaves because he'd been a teenager!

356p

Abraham resembles Shakespeare: a barely-educated man who was a deathless writer. If Lincoln had lived three centuries earlier, numerous theories would suggest another man — maybe Seward — as the "true Lincoln."

402p

Winnie is in charge of the compost pile, and has decreed: "The bears are awake. We won't compost any more fruit or eggshells."

16:D

Lincoln was rich! At the time of his wedding, in 1842, he made $1200 a year — equal to the governor's salary. By the 1850s, his income reached $5,000. But Abraham was unfulfilled. He had "the hypo" — his term for depression (then called "hypochondria"). His whole life was somehow incomplete. That's why he was drawn into politics.

McPherson's clever plan is to focus on several key decisions: Lincoln's response to the Southern secession, the reinforcing of Fort Sumter, the Emancipation Proclamation.

Abe was an autocratic leader, one must admit. He didn't *trust* Congress to suspend habeas corpus; he issued a decree. And why couldn't the House and Senate have passed the Emancipation Proclamation? As it is, the document had dubious constitutionality.

17:D

Last night I dreamed Bob Dylan was smoking four cigarettes simultaneously. I was at a party with him, and actually spoke to him. At one point, Dylan removed one of the cigarettes, and held it between his fingers. The other three remained firmly in his mouth. (The cigarettes were fairly short.) Dylan had a cautious grin.

503p
Today is a trampling rain, a heedless rain. Grange and I sat on the sofa looking out the living room window. Trees and shrubs twisted in pain. It was like watching a naked woman being flogged.

18:D

At a party, a man named Jerry asked me: "What are Gog and Magog?"
"I've heard of them," I replied, "but I'm not exactly sure. Maybe two giants in Genesis?"
Jerry had been told that I'm a history lover.

418p
Now I've looked Gog and Magog up in *Collier's Encyclopedia*:

> These were the names, respectively, of a king and of his supposed kingdom, mentioned several times in Ezekiel 38 and 39, and once in the Apocalypse (20:7). In the first passage of Ezekiel we find the command of Yahweh to the prophet: "Son of man, set thy face against Gog of the land of Magog...and prophesy of him...Behold, I come against thee, O Gog, the chief prince of Mosoch and Thubal" (38:2-3). These two chapters contain repeated reference to

Gog and Magog, but they furnish only vague and uncertain indications as to the identity of the ruler or the location of the country.

Picking up Ezekiel, God seems furious with Gog (perhaps due to the similarity of their names?):

Thou shalt fall upon the mountains of Israel, thou, and all thy bands, and the people that is with thee: I will give thee unto the ravenous birds of every sort, and to the beasts of the field to be devoured.

God gets so angry that he loses control of His grammar.

19:D

Grange and I saw the "Midsummer Night's Dream" ballet in Kingston. We were both enchanted. My son didn't 't understand the plot, but he believes in fairies, and found Puck achingly funny. Professional dancers played the lead roles, and Titania, the Fairy Queen, was ravishing.

On the way home, we encountered a coyote. Though I've lived here seven years, it's the first coyote I've seen. He crossed in front of our car, then remained on the side of the road, watching us. He didn't look like Wile E. Coyote from the Roadrunner cartoons — deep brown and attenuated. Rather, he resembled a wary dog.

Afterwards, I pondered if there was some connection between Puck and the coyote; a message the night was offering?

503p

That splinter which bedeviled me a week ago has now completely disappeared. Perhaps when you forget about splinters, they quietly extract themselves.

20:D

Winnie has a collection of essential oils in the cabinet above the bathroom sink. (She once took an aromatherapy class.) Today I decided: "I will put a little spearmint oil in my bath." But when I looked at the oils

— all in squat brown glass bottles with black tops — the words on the labels had rubbed off. Oil dissolves its own name.

21:D

I awoke this morning wearing only one sock. One of my socks fell off while I slumbered. My feet felt awkwardly unequal.

413p
History is a street. At one end a tribe sits in a circle, telling stories. At the other end, children speak on cellphones and play *Grand Theft Auto IV*. Between these two terminuses are all the people who ever lived.

A street has two directions; you may walk either way. But almost everyone walks forward on this street. Only historians walk backwards.

506p
Have you ever noticed how slow crows fly? They fly like Muppets on *Sesame Street* — as if suspended from half-invisible strings!

619p
Lately I suspect that my wife and I have one of the Great Loves. History records few major romances. Even Romeo and Juliet are fictitious. And the concept of a Great Love seems archaic today; one can't imagine such a bond in the world of YouTube. But perhaps true lovers persist, hidden from the intrusive media.

22:D

A cement truck is always festive — particularly one that's spinning. Grange realizes this, and so do I. Today we found a cement truck on our road, and stopped together, struck by masculine awe.

451p
Last night I dreamed I was part of a plan to "set up" the Kingpin Of Crime, the glowering Marvel Comics villain. I arrived at a penthouse in Manhattan, where my friend Delia was patiently folding papers and putting them in envelopes. She sat at the kitchen table — and beneath the table was... Spider-Man! He said something reassuring to me like: "Don't worry,

I'll protect you once those goons arrive!" Spidey seemed quite small, too brightly colored and fake. But I noticed his Queens accent, just before I woke up.

619p
My wife teases me about how quickly I injure umbrellas. "If I could take out life insurance on an umbrella, I would," Winnie said today.

But it's true. I haven't held a new umbrella 25 minutes and one of its ribs is sticking out. How this happens, I don't understand. I just open and close umbrellas, like everyone else. I don't go charging into telephone poles with them. But invariably, they break in my hands.

23:D

Grange found a small bird on the lawn today. He brought it in to me, holding it delicately. The bird had a yellow head, and a gray belly. "It's not dead," Grange said — because it was still warm.

I touched its soft feathers just once, and stared at its chest. The bird did not breathe.

But who can know for certain if any creature is alive?

631p
Winnie looked up the bird in *The Sibley Guide to Birds*. He's a Black-Throated Green Warbler (*Dendroica virens*), she believes.

24:D

My dental hygienist saw Bob Dylan. I went for my biannual cleaning today, and learned that she attended a concert last summer with her husband, at Bethel Woods.

"How was he?" I wondered.

"He was good," she smiled. "But Bethel Woods is very commercial. It costs five dollars for a bottle of water!"

Ironically, this arena is on the site of the original Woodstock — which was free.

426p
Crows must sleep, because you never hear them in deep night.

533p

I had some extra time at the library at New Paltz, so I went looking in the stacks, where I found a book with the stirring title, *Heraldic Visitations of Wales*. It's a series of coats of arms, with notations in Welsh. I copied one out:

> Dos yn iach, y darlleydd mwyn glan ar hynn o amsser, ni
> ddown i ben fyth roi digon o glod i'r hael, a digon o anglod
> ir kvbvddion drwg.

Lovely, isn't it?

622p

I just finished *The Fatal Bullet: A True Account of the Assassination, Lingering Pain, Death and Burial of James A. Garfield, Twentieth President of the United States. Also Including The Inglorious Life and Career of the Despised Assassin Guiteau*. It's a graphic novel by Rick Geary, from the series "A Treasury of Victorian Murder." It has unnerving revelations: Guiteau lived at the Oneida Community in upstate New York, throughout the Civil War! (Why? Because he was raised according to the philosophy of the Reverend John H. Noyes, ideologue of the community.) "In keeping with Rev. Noyes' ideals, marital monogamy had been abandoned for a system by which a member could enter into several simultaneous 'spiritual marriages;' accordingly, Charles Guiteau entered three such unions." (But these "spiritual marriages" involved sex!)

Three American presidents were murdered within 36 years: in 1865, 1880, 1901. The USA was like one of those unstable Latin American countries.

Guiteau shot poor Garfield in the back! This was at the Baltimore and Potomac Depot in Washington, DC, as the president prepared to go on vacation: Saturday, July 2, 1880.

The bullet fractured the president's 11th and 12th ribs, chipped his first lumbar vertebra, penetrated a major artery, and finally came to rest just behind his pancreas. Garfield could have easily survived, but his doctors were massively incompetent. (And maybe he lost the will to live?)

Though Guiteau was likely insane, there was a political logic to his assassination. At that point, the Republican Party was deeply divided between the "half-breeds," who advocated reform, and the conservative "stalwarts." (That's how Garfield came to the White House — the Republican convention was deadlocked, and he was chosen as a compromise. He was the only sitting congressman ever elected president!) On the evening of May 18, Guiteau suddenly received what he called an "impression" that if Garfield could be eliminated, the Republican Party would reunite. He felt that he was the agent of God in this regard. The book doesn't address this question, but I suspect Guiteau's plan succeeded. "Letters of praise and support arrived daily" for him at the District Jail! Sometimes insane maniacs really are hearing the voice of God.

25:D

I drove down to New York City, down Route 17, as usual. There's a riot of shopping malls and box stores with names like Carpet World and Tile City. The Sears sign has one dark letter, so you see:

SEA S

603p
Winnie told me a story about her father: "One day he took a five dollar bill out of his pocket, set it in an ashtray, and lit it on fire. The whole family watched as the money burned. Then there was silence. Finally, my father spoke: 'We don't have much money, but we don't live for money, either.' I never forgot that."

26:D

Why were three American presidents shot between 1865 and 1901, and none for the next 62 years? Because the late 19th century was when a vital American democracy was being hijacked by boundless corporate power. (The euphemism in history books is "The Gilded Age.") The three assassins expressed a revolutionary disgust with the presidency. (One of them, Leon Czolgosz, was an actual anarchist.)

412p
Grange and I walked in the woods today. He's now old enough to sit completely still. So we sat beside a tree and watched as a shiny black bird dropped down from another tree. (I write "dropped down" because she

didn't seem to fly.) Then she began to rummage through the leaf cover, pulling up leaves with her beak, and hoisting them into the air. Her motions were almost comical — like an enraged husband searching for his car keys. I suppose she was hunting for grubs and worms.

Finally, unsatisfied, she flew off to our left, with startling speed. (Guessing from her dark coloring, I've given her a female pronoun.)

27:D

Twice today, I poked myself in the right eye. The first time, a corner of my briefcase came too close to my face. Afterwards, my right eye was tearing.

Grange looked up at me, and asked: "Are you sad, Daddy?" "No," I answered, honestly. "I just hurt my eye a little bit."

Then I sat for the next three minutes, weeping on one side.

702p
Winnie bought a snakeskin belt last week. (She found it at a thrift store, so she isn't responsible for the murder of snakes.) It's tan, composed of little diamond shapes, with darker brown markings resembling Nike insignias.

Today the belt was curled on a chair in the living room — just like a true snake!

741p
I took a shit, and when I peered down into the toilet, saw an ant climbing up the white wall. Could this insect have emerged from my feces? It's impossible, I'm sure.

29:D

Winnie and I began to have sex last night, when suddenly there was a furious sound just outside our house. It sounded like a cat barking. It's difficult to have sex while a wild creature is snarling 12 feet away. We both stopped, and listened.

Then the sound died away, and I touched Winnie's thigh.

614p
Grange's happiness is so wide and broad. He's not cheery all the time, but when he is, it's almost a planetary happiness. In comparison, my own joy is like a small mousehole. The size of our happiness shrinks as we age.

30:D

Gettysburg: The Graphic Novel, by a young, serious-looking fellow named C. M. Butzer, is a careful, rather scholarly — but elegiac — description of that battle, in black, white, and faint blue washes. Dramatically, it contains the *entire* Gettysburg Address.

I suspect comic books are the easiest way to understand geographical history. Even though I have twice visited Gettysburg, I never realized that it's a big bowl. The entire battle hinged on one decision by Union General John Buford. As Butzer puts it:

> The advancing Confederate Army overwhelmed the Union's meager forces and chased them out of Gettysburg. General Buford knew this would happen. He did not need to win the day but only hold on long enough for reinforcements to arrive and secure the highly defensible Cemetery Ridge.

In other words, whoever controlled the high ground in this large valley must win the battle. At this point, Robert E. Lee, the supposedly brilliant general, was a fool. General James Longstreet said to him, "All we have to do is throw our army around by their left and we shall interpose between the Federal Army and Washington." He replied: "No, if the enemy is there, then we must attack him there. They are there in position, and I am going to whip them or they are going to whip me."

Lee *ceded* the high ground to the enemy! No wonder they smashed him to pieces during Pickett's Charge! ("Over 12,000 rebel soldiers participated in the assault; less than half of them were able to retreat.") Deep inside, Robert E. Lee knew his cause was unjust, and wanted to lose — nobly, heroically, but decisively. At the end of the battle, half to himself, Lee exclaimed: "I never saw troops behave more magnificently. If they had been supported as they were to have been — but, for some reason not yet fully explained to me, were not — we would have held the position and the day would have been ours. Too bad! Too bad! Oh! Too bad!" Then, with bowed head, he entered his tent (through a wooden door).

"Too bad!" What an insufficient phrase, for three days and 40,000 casualties.

Gettysburg: The Graphic Novel walks the line between deploring the gruesome waste of war and honoring the greatness of Lincoln, and of the

Union troops, for defeating slavery. Like many Civil War comic books, it comes with footnotes — luckily, because otherwise I would have skipped othe subtlest panel, which only has the title "June 30, 1863. Gettysburg, Pennsylvania." The note reads: "The opening page is a depiction of the Union cavalry riding into the small town of Gettysburg. The region's few freemen (freed African Americans) are leaving the town in anticipation of a Confederate invasion. During the Civil War, runaway slaves and free African Americans captured by the Confederates were treated harshly; they were frequently marched back to the South and forced into slave labor." Let us not forget, the Civil War had many elements, but one was savage racism.

414p
Twice today I found an ant in the toilet bowl. One cannot avoid suspecting that pee tastes good to ants.

2:E

History holds us in its vise. No one notices this. We believe we are free to see any movie we want, but we can only see the movies of 2006.

And our thoughts will only be the thoughts of 2006.

621p
A small blackberry bush is growing in our front yard. The berries are ripe, but full of thick pits, unlike the ones in supermarkets. Nature created sweetness embedded with woody pellets.

3:E

And today — 8 ants in the toilet bowl! (Although only one in the water.)

Winnie read in a natural healing book that if ants are attracted to your urine, it's a sign of diabetes. Could she, Grange or I be diabetic?

617p
A comic book edits action into a series of static poses. As you read the comic, your mind fills in all the missing movements. It's like seeing snapshots from a ballet and imagining the dance.

4:E

Today I saw my friend Phil. Grange and I were walking on the road when he stopped in his pickup truck. "How are you?" I asked.

"Good," he said. "But I'm supposed to be in Africa."

I wasn't sure if he was joking. Phil must have known from the look on my face, because he continued: "Really! I should be in Africa."

"Where in Africa?"

"Zimbabwe. But it's a long story. Have a good day!"

And he drove off.

614p

A voice on my answering machine: "Hi, this is Kathy with Financial Freedom..."

5:E

I saw a sobering sight by the sink this morning. One ant was carrying another, the same size as himself. Slowly I realized the inert ant was dead. The carrier-ant reached the edge of the sink and deposited his burden, so that the insect corpse rested upside down with one leg crooked, hooked on to the counter.

Then the living creature marched off. Was this a silent ant funeral?

612p

Kathy with Financial Freedom called again, and left a second message. She's starting to become real to me. I can picture Kathy in her cubicle in St. Paul, Minnesota, dutifully dialing numbers.

6:E

Last night I slept poorly, so I spent hours listening to my wife sleep: her snufflings, sputters and snores. It occurred to me that if my wife *only* slept — if she never awoke — I would divorce her.

617p

Today I was walking in the backyard when a snake crossed my path. It was a thin, harmless garter snake — just for a moment I glimpsed its coil — but I sensed the Shadow of Death.

7:E

My wife went away to visit her aunt. She took Grange, so I'm alone for two days. It's so easy to make the bed, in her absence! And at the end of the day, there's only two bowls to wash.

I suppose this is why people live alone.

On the other hand, late at night I begin to fear that an assassin is waiting in the front yard with a blowgun.

8:E

History is relatively recent, as we use the term. The concept of history as an exact record began in the Enlightenment. Heroic tales — like *The Iliad* — are quite old, and so are precise records (dating back at least to Sumeria) but the combination of the two originated in the 18th century. Shakespeare's "history plays" are more like ingenious fables than historical accounts – because he was inspired by Raphael Holinshead, who himself wrote mythically.

9:E

Winnie and I sat in our yard to eat lunch yesterday. I noticed a creature walking parallel to us 30 feet away. I assumed this was a cat, but my wife said: "Look, a fox!" The creature was narrow and starved-looking: a red fox with a gray tail. For a moment, it even walked towards us!

A fox in midday; we gaped at her silently.

10:E

Every word is a historical document. The word "dough," for example, originated centuries ago in the Old English word *dāg*. The "gh" is a historical artifact, like a Druid burial site — a relic of the fifth century.

503p

Today Grange and I went for a walk, and found the largest tribe of motherless deer I've ever seen: I counted 14. They were all yearlings, the smallest one the size of a German shepherd. Four or five of them stared at us, then they all ran east, in profile — looking like Persian relief sculptures.

Where was their mother? Killed, or on vacation?

11:E

At the Sojourner Truth Library I found a hermetic volume: *Itinerary of General Washington from June 15, 1775 to December 23, 1783* by William S. Baker, published by Hunterdon House in Lambertville, New Jersey. The original copyright is 1892 by William Spohn Baker, but the book was reprinted in 1970. One of the first pages I opened to was:

> Sunday, June 18.
> At Springfield: Orderly Book. — "As it is at all times of great importance both for the sake of appearance and for the regularity of service that the different military Ranks should be distinguished from each other and more especially at present,
> "The Commander in Chief has thought proper to establish the following distinctions and strongly recommends it to all the Officers to endeavor to Conform to them as speedily as possible.
> "The Major General to wear a blue coat with Buff facings and lining — yellow buttons — white or buff undercloaths and two Epaulets, with two Stars upon each and a black and white Feather in the Hat.
> "The Brigadier Generals the same uniform as the Major Generals with the difference of one Star instead of two and a white feather.
> "The Colonels, Lieutenant Colonels and Majors the uniforms of their regiments and two Epaulettes.
> "The Captains: the uniforms of their regiments and an Epaulette on the right shoulder.
> "The subalterns, — the uniform of their regiment and an Epaulette on the left shoulder."

One of Washington's tasks was creating the uniforms of his officers — as if he were the costume designer of a musical comedy!

12:E

Besides flying, some birds can super-walk. This morning I saw a sparrow on my front lawn skittering at enormous speed: at least 11 mph! Then she flew.

No matter how fast a bird walks, I wouldn't call it "running." There's no muscular flexing of the legs.

452p
Our nation's capital is named "Washington," and so is one of our distant states. Also seven mountains, eight streams, ten lakes, 33 counties, nine colleges and 121 American towns and villages bear this name (according to *George Washington: Man and Monument* by Marcus Cunliffe). We're lucky our whole damn country isn't called "Washingtonia"!

13:E

I'm reading *Jazz: A Critic's Guide to the 100 Most Important Recordings* by Ben Ratliff. On Louis Armstrong's first recordings, with Kid Oliver, he plays cornet and slide whistle. If the history of jazz had deviated slightly, Armstrong would have been the finest slide whistle player in history.

331p
Where was Thomas Jefferson during the Revolutionary war? Did he fight? He was certainly young. One never hears about Jefferson in uniform. Was he one of those revolutionaries who asks everyone else to carry a gun while he stays home writing manifestoes?

339p
I've never seen so many robins as this spring. A small tribe of them hug the woods around my house. Often, as you step outside, a robin shoots out at an oblique angle — always flying low. Grange loves them, and believes it's always the same robin. I can tell from the word he uses ("robba") and the look on his face.

And maybe it *is* always the same robin. Grange may be correct.

15:E

Jefferson was governor of Virginia during the Revolution.

456p
I just read an essay on Herbert Hoover in *Harpers*. What a story! Orphaned as a child, raised by a cruel uncle, he stumbled upon a mystical

map to a gold mine in Burma, and suddenly had $25 million! Then he led relief efforts in Bolshevik Russia! Why doesn't every schoolchild learn this?

17:E

I'm back with *Jazz: A Critic's Guide to the 100 Most Important Recordings*. I never realized how short the history of jazz is. Half of its span is the lifetime of Louis Armstrong! I mention Louis, because he pioneered the jazz solo. Or as Ratliff writes (parenthetically): "If Armstrong didn't invent the solo, he invented the importance of the solo and its function as a kind of musical heroism." Jazz might have evolved in other directions besides the solo form. It could have been an ensemble music, like African drumming.

Because jazz history is so brief, each virtuoso deeply affects it. Without Miles Davis, jazz might have a different definition today.

Music is tricky to describe in words — it's worse even than God. Much of Ratliff's criticism involves the distinction between a harmonic approach and a melodic one. No matter how well he writes, you can't hear the solo in your mind from his description.

Jazz is constantly in danger of spilling out of its genre — into pop music or "contemporary Classical." Ratliff weirdly believes that Cecil Taylor's music is not jazz; it's too way-out. This book may be read as a history of 20th century America, which began absolutely racist and eventually bestowed the Presidential Medal of Freedom on Duke Ellington in 1969 (given by Nixon!). Ellington deserved the award, because he almost single-handedly willed jazz into art, long before anyone imagined this music had compositional complexity.

The first jazz concert at the White House wasn't until 1978, under Jimmy Carter!

Did you know that 1959 was the preeminent year for jazz recordings — the equivalent of 1939 for movies? Besides Miles Davis' *Kind of Blue*, John Coltrane put out *Giant Steps*, Charles Mingus released *Blues and Roots*, Ornette Coleman recorded *The Shape of Jazz to Come*, *The Complete Billie Holiday on Verve 1945-1959* came out, *Sonny Rollins Trio in Sweden 1959* — plus Duke Ellington scored *Anatomy of a Murder*!

This "critic's guide" has a self-hating prejudice against white jazz musicians. Ratliff is almost mortified to include Dave Brubeck, and says of Chet Baker: "Baker's technical talent was slender and his sound

42

unrelievedly wan" — which is cruel and baseless. And he never mentions the genius of Paul Desmond, Brubeck's serene saxophonist.

My main disagreements are the omission of Joe Henderson, one of the most subtle living jazzmen, and the wonderfully chaotic Rahsaan Roland Kirk. (But both these gentlemen are mentioned on other musicians' albums — and Henderson is named in "Another 100 More Albums You Should Own, or At Least Know About.") Leaving out Fats Waller is criminal, even if he is on the "Another 100" list. And I would have preferred more soul-jazz, like Cannonball Adderley, and political artists like Gil Scott-Heron. I never intended to actually read this book, just to browse it, but Ratliff's writing hooked me. Here is a typical anecdote:

> I once asked Borah Bergman, the pianist, why so many free-jazz musicians played in duos. He thought about *Interstellar Space* [by John Coltrane], and he thought about different motivations of players from completely different schools, until he got completely muddled. Then a few days later, he faxed me a one-word answer: "economics."

Sadly, the list trails off in the last couple decades. (The book was published in 2002.) As Ratliff suggests in his review of Albert Ayler's *Live in Greenwich Village: The Complete Impulse Recordings*, jazz may be attenuating because of a failure of definition. Much actual jazz today is termed "trip-hop," "trance" or "noise bands."

18:E

Perhaps all historical problems are questions of definition. Monarchism didn't exactly end; arguably, the American Republic simply extended monarchism, by electing the monarch. Just as Disco may be seen as a form of Rock, representative democracy may be a reworking of kingship.

Another way to describe jazz (which Ratliff does not employ) uses the metaphor of temperature. "Hot jazz" is distinct from "cool jazz," or even "lukewarm" or "tepid" jazz (though I've never heard the phrase "cold jazz" — is that an oxymoron?). The "hotness" concept is suggested by jazz nicknames like "Red Garland" and "Pepper Adams." A critic might attempt a precise measurement of each album: "*The Gerry Mulligan Quartet: Volume 1* has a temperature of 59°."

618p

Tonight the western sky was smeared with blood — a sanguinary sunset.

19:E

A pained-looking woman in Kingston handed me a leaflet entitled "Never Receive 666: The Mark of the Beast." It has small, smeary print and several diagrams. The first shows a barcode imprinted on a man's forehead; the second depicts a man's hand with a slot in it for inserting a credit card. The third is a diagram of a microchip. The anonymous zealot who wrote this tract gets to the point quickly: "The mark will be a barcode, and the number will be 666" — that's the very first sentence. By the end of the paragraph we learn, "The 'cashless society' will come into effect soon!!!" Throughout this essay, in fact, is a terror of the disappearance of money. Apparently currency is one of the few bulwarks against the Antichrist.

With a credit card, some supervising intelligence can watch you at all times. But if you steal $30 from your aunt, you run out of the house and the money is yours, to use freely. Satan loves credit cards, because Satan needs slaves. But God believes in money, because God loves freedom.

451p

Sometimes Winnie will start laughing just looking at a deck of cards. The other day, she opened a deck and pointed to the Queen of Clubs: "See that look on her face? Don't you think she has to fart?" Then she laughed for five minutes.

27:E

I've been reading that "Never Receive 666" pamphlet again. I came upon this section:

> Another system that has been designed to work along with
> the "smart card" is called "vein reading." The system uses
> the veins in the back of the hand or wrist to certify that the
> person presenting the card is authorized to use it.

I never heard of this identification system. (Iris-scanning is used in the film *Minority Report*.) But sure enough, vein reading is real! I saw it on the Internet: a soda machine where a Japanese girl thrusts her hand into an aperture, which scans her veins.

31:E

Grange and I went to a parade in Stone Ridge, where three bagpipers played a familiar song. Afterwards, I searched for the name of this quintessential bagpipe tune. I Googled "the most popular song in the bagpipe" but it's "Amazing Grace." One website referred to "Scotland the Brave" as "the unofficial national anthem of Scotland," so I listened to a version on YouTube. Voilà! It was my song.

The video was illustrated with Scottish military uniforms. How noble and manly they are! I had the sudden urge to go off to war and fight with my comrades for Scottish freedom.

Are there lyrics to "Scotland the Brave"?, I wondered. Of course there are — written around 1950 by the Scottish journalist Cliff Hanley (about fifty years after the song first appeared). Here's the chorus:

> Towering in gallant fame,
> Scotland my mountain hame,
> High may your proud standards gloriously wave;
> Land of my high endeavour,
> Land of the shining river,
> Land of my heart for ever, Scotland the brave.

What a fine surprise, the word "hame"!

1:F

Grange is such a fast walker. Actually, he mostly doesn't walk — he runs, skips, canters. It's only after a mile that he begins to flag, and I become a better walker than he.

In only four years, one can outrun one's father!

359p

I heard a salute to Oscar Peterson, the jazz pianist, on WAMU. I never knew how fast he played, with his trio! (I'd only heard his witty accompaniment of Ella Fitzgerald and Louis Armstrong.) Peterson played at such a clip that it was almost no longer jazz. It was like a language spoken so fast that it's unintelligible. He invented an avant-garde of speed.

3:F

And now I've read *another* Lincolnian graphic novel: *The Murder of Abraham Lincoln* by Rick Geary, illustrator of the Garfield treatise. Geary's book is quite detailed — a little *too* detailed for a short (though unpaginated) comic. The story of Guiteau was simple and bizarre, but Lincoln was killed by a conspiracy, so there's too many characters (plus John Wilkes Booth's meandering flight after the assassination). Nonetheless, near-unbelievable details embellish this story, apparently influenced by William Hanchett's *The Lincoln Murder Conspiracies*:

1) Booth carried a derringer with a single bullet in it.

2) He was quite drunk at the time of the murder.

3) Fifteen couples turned down the offer to accompany Abe and Mary to the theater that night, until Miss Clara Harris and her fiancé, Major Henry R. Rathbone, agreed.

4) Immediately after Lincoln was shot, his wife was prostrate with grief. Miss Laura Keene (the star of the play they'd been watching) entered the Presidential Box and cradled Abraham's head in her lap.

5) Booth, reading the latest newspapers the day after the murder, was "surprised and disappointed" to discover that he was not hailed as a hero in the South. In fact he was universally condemned as a villain!

6) The appointment calendar which Booth used as a diary during his 12 days as a fugitive was brought to Secretary of War Stanton, in whose possession it disappeared, only to resurface two years later, with 18 pages missing!

7) Lincoln's funeral train stopped in numerous unlikely places: Jersey City, N.J.; Poughkeepsie, N.Y.; Albany, N.Y.; Columbus, OH; Indianapolis, IN.

8) An enterprising photographer took an image of Lincoln's corpse as it lay in the Great Rotunda in New York City. Edwin M. Stanton ordered the plates seized and destroyed.

One of the artist's successes is building up the suspense about Lincoln's bodyguards. William Crook of the Metropolitan police, his usual guard, leaves before his replacement, John F. Parker, arrives. But Parker disappears during *Our American Cousin* and is spotted in the balcony of the theater, on the sidewalk outside, and at a nearby tavern. Lincoln's attendant, Charles Forbes, guards the doors to the box where Abe sits. John Wilkes Booth is so famous he simply hands his business card to Forbes and is immediately allowed in.

Clearly, we are discussing a conspiracy here. But is it possible that John Wilkes Booth, that unstable, egomaniacal and deeply romantic character, was the absolute apex of the conspiracy? Where did *he* get his money? Clearly, someone was supporting him.

Is it possible that Lincoln arranged his own murder? He was a depressive man, who had just survived an anguishing war. He knew Reconstruction would be difficult and that he'd be reviled by all. Why not die a martyr, and guarantee citizenship for African-Americans, in the ensuing adulation? Why else would he invent this bogus "premonitory dream" three days before his death, in which he sees a black coffin in the White House, asks the guard, "Who is dead in the White House?" and receives the cold reply: "The president. He has been killed by an assassin." Why else would he tell his bodyguard the day of his death: "Crook, do you know, I believe there are men who want to take my life — and I've no doubt they will do it"? Why else would he arrange to die on Good Friday, on the full moon?

Another possibility: John Wilkes Booth was his ex-lover!

It's embarrassing — almost humiliating — to learn history from comic books, but it's certainly easy. Luckily I'm not a "real" historian.

231p
The wild strawberries are ripe, behind our house. Why don't the birds eat them? Are they too stupid?

4:F

John Wilkes Booth was the perfect assassin for Lincoln. Flamboyant, racist, handsome, he was the character Sheakespeare would have created to murder Abraham.. Only J. W. B. could have killed Lincoln; anyone else's bullet would have missed. Booth was the murderer out of central casting (literally!).

Lincoln's murder was a crime of passion. Booth was drunk, and in a state of rage and exaltation. Just before he died, he seemed to repent the deed: "Tell my mother that I die for my country... I did what I thought was best..." He sounds like someone who's shot his girlfriend.

5:F

Nowadays Grange constantly carries a small plastic knight, which he calls "Knighty." This character wears a silver suit of armor; his face is hidden. Knighty gives Grange courage.

"Knighty wants to walk!" Grange announced, so of course we went. Knighty led the way. That is, Grange walked ahead of me and held his plastic knight in front of him, at arm's length.

Knighty led us to a stump, where we sat completely still. "Dragon is coming!" Knighty explained. After seven minutes, a squirrel emerged from behind a tree. "That's the dragon," Knighty whispered. We held our breath. The squirrel climbed to the top of the tree.

6:F

Lincoln loved the theater. Often in the evening, he'd leave the White House and drop in on a play, just for 20 minutes (usually a comedy). Men who grow up in the long dark nights of the forest appreciate theatrical glamour. Lincoln's affection for theater killed him.

349p
Lincoln's murder was truly Hitchcockian. Geary's comic — in fact, the cover! — stresses this view. Lincoln sits in the theater, watching a performance, the yellowish stage lights reflected in his face. Behind him, Booth stealthily pushes open a door with his elbow, clutching a derringer, a look of vindictive madness on his face.

The most disquieting moment in the *The Murder of Abraham Lincoln* is when Booth slips in behind the Presidential Box earlier that day and "uses his penknife to bore a tiny hole in the inner door to the box... through which he can view the occupants as they watch the play." We see the assassin peering through the hole — a disembodied eye.

515p
Lincoln's death was an act of race-hatred. What inspired Booth was Lincoln's assertion on April 11, 1865 that African-Americans would become citizens.

48

7:F

80% of chainsaw injuries take place on the left side of the body, I learned today in the *Olive Press*.

503p
Grange and I walked outside, and as soon as we stepped towards the woods, 29 sparrows flew up from the grass. (I'm not certain of the number, and I'm not even sure they were sparrows. They were small, they fluttered, they were almost soundless. Rather than calling them "sparrows," I should say "little fluttering beings.")

536p
I can easily imagine Lincoln listening to jazz — but it would be slow, melancholic jazz. The music of... Chet Baker!

8:F

"My grandparents were sure Lincoln was Jewish," Arthur told me. "They emigrated here from Odessa in 1914. When they heard that there was a president named Abraham who had a Hasidic beard and always wore black, they knew he was a Jew."

And maybe they were right! One of Lincoln's ancestors was Levi Lincoln, born in Hingham in 1749. Another Lincoln was named Mordecai (who had a son also named Mordecai). Levi is a tribe of Jewish priests! And how many non-Jews have the name Mordecai? Of course, Abraham and his sister Sarah were named after the two founders of the Jewish faith. (Plus Lincoln had two typically Jewish traits: non-drinking and depression.)

Has anyone ever seriously pursued the theory that Lincoln was a crypto-Jew? It's possible his ancestors were Jewish, converted long ago, but maintaining some Hebraic traditions.

417p
Grange and I were in the woods today, by a clearing, when a group of five deer approached. We stood perfectly still. The deer stared at us, then chose to trust us. Eventually, they migrated towards a patch of violets and

feasted. The largest one, which stood closest, began to shit — just like a cow shits, standing up, pouring out feces in a stream.

I'd never been close enough to watch a deer defecate.

9:F

As of June 1, the second best-selling DVD in America was *Barbie and the Three Musketeers*. Did anyone else notice this? (One of my patients left *The Wall Street Journal* today.)

503p
At this point, deer have only one natural enemy: automobiles.

752p
I went out this morning, with my umbrella. (I'm one of the few residents of Stone Ridge who owns an umbrella.) In the light rain, I walked 40 feet into the woods and stood looking at 700 trees.

An hour later, I walked out again, and the rain was now wind. Yes, rain can transform into wind. It has that spiritual power.

13:F

My wife bought an olive green cake of soap with the words "Kiss My Face" on it. But the second word is in smaller letters, and there are no spaces between the words, so it looks like:

KISSmyFACE

as if that were all one word. It's a clever idea, to make a phrase into a word by alternating capitals and small letters. Here's my new brand of soap:

WITHmaliceTOWARDnone

603p
Later I lay under a sugar maple in the backyard, reading Abraham Lincoln's *Speeches and Writings*. Then I set down my book and listened. The trees were calling to one another, using the voices of birds.

O how peaceful is June, upon this unfurling earth!

15:F

Arthur's father served in the Korean War. "He was stationed in El Paso, Texas, and all the enlisted men lived in huts," Harry explained. "There were separate huts for the 'fairies' — that's what Dad called the gay men. This was in 1951."

I wonder if "Don't ask, don't tell" goes back to the Roman Empire?

703p

I took a bath today, as rain battered on the roof. The water was desperate to break into my house, like a bear tempted by a peanut butter and jelly sandwich on the seat of a Volkswagen. But the roof held.

16:F

Crows don't sing; they talk.

459p

Arthur bought *The Life of Daniel Defoe: A Critical Biography* by John Richetti. I was looking through it yesterday, at his house. Defoe, who invented the novel (in the form of a hoax, *Robinson Crusoe*) was nothing like a contemporary "literary figure." He probably died without realizing he was a "great writer." (In fact, he died in seclusion, apparently hiding from creditors.) But he was similar to modern people in one way — he was a blogger, or, in 18th-century parlance, a "pamphleteer." He wrote so many essays, almost always anonymous or pseudonymous, that no one knows exactly which are his. We're pretty certain he published pamphlets attacking himself, or quoting himself. It's possible that Defoe could not have enumerated what he'd written. Richetti believes his crowning achievement is *A Tour Thro' the Whole Island of Great Britain* — which contains large sections plagiarized from other writers.

How refreshing, that writers were once like criminals!

18:F

Recently I compiled this list:

First Names of the Presidents

George
John
Thomas
James
James
John
Andrew
Martin
William
John
James
Zachary
Millard
Franklin
James
Abraham
Andrew
Ulysses
Rutherford
James
Chester
Grover
Benjamin
Grover
William
Theodore
William
Woodrow
Warren
Calvin
Herbert
Franklin
Harry
Dwight
John
Lyndon

Richard
Gerald
James
Ronald
George
Bill
George
Barack

I've never seen this list anywhere. Now is a good time to compile it, while Barack is still President. It's delightful to have all of American history leading up to this holy Muslim name.

Some Presidents had exotic names — and usually in clumps. "Abraham Andrew Ulysses Rutherford," for example. I never knew that "Harry" was Truman's actual given name.

Clearly "James" wins, numerically.

This list reminds us that each president was an actual person, born of a mother, eating oatmeal. "President Buchanan" is an august, honorable leader; "James" a two-legged man.

19:F

Grange and I met a snake on the road today. It was painfully small — perhaps young? — no bigger than a long worm. At first I thought it *was* a worm, but it had a more pronounced head and a mesmerizing style of locomotion, undulating in perfect waves. Grange gave me his Smile of Triumph. Young boys appreciate the ingenuity of reptiles.

503p
Did George Washington literally lead the American Revolution while wearing a powdered wig? I believe so. Clearly the concept of a revolutionary has changed over the centuries.

20:F

Have you noticed that animals take turns appearing? The days that the deer are walking, the squirrels hide, and vice versa. If a fox runs, no other creature will be visible. It's as if they're following the rules of theater — animals don't upstage each other.

452p

At least since the 16th century, military bands have accompanied soldiers as they marched into war. I wonder if, in the heat of battle, Napoleon's musicians ever produced something we'd now call "jazz"?

21:F

I copied this out of *Viewpoints on Abraham Lincoln*, edited by Roger Melanson:

> In 1872, Colonel Ward H. Lamon published his *Life of Abraham Lincoln*. Colonel Lamon ... [was] Lincoln's friend and acquaintance of years. When the President-elect started for Washington, Colonel Lamon had charge of the arrangements. Lincoln appointed him Marshal of the District of Columbia. When the body of the martyred President was carried back to Springfield, Colonel Lamon was in charge of the funeral train. In addition to being qualified by knowledge to write the life of his chief and friend, he had another advantage. He had the benefit of the collection of manuscripts pertaining to Lincoln gathered by William H. Herndon, who knew the real Lincoln better than any other man. Lamon... knew his subject, and he waited seven years to publish his book, giving great attention to accuracy. Here is an excerpt:
> "The community in which he lived was preeminently a community of Freethinkers in matters of religion; and it was no secret, nor has it been a secret since, that Mr. Lincoln agreed with the majority of his associates in denying the authority of divine revelation. It was his honest belief, a belief which it was no reproach to hold in New Salem, Anno Domini 1834, and one which he never thought of concealing. It was no distinction, either good or bad, no honor, and no shame. But he had made himself thoroughly familiar with the writings of Paine and Volney — the Ruins by the one, and The Age of Reason by the other. His mind was full of the subject, and he felt an

itching to write. He did write, and the result was a little book. It was probably merely an extended essay, but it is ambitiously spoken of as 'a book' by himself and by the persons who were made acquainted with its contents. In this work he intended to demonstrate —
    "First, that the Bible is not God's revelation.
    "Second, that Jesus was not the son of God.'
    "No leaf of this volume has survived. Mr. Lincoln carried it in manuscript to the store of Samuel Hill, where it was read and discussed. Hill was himself an unbeliever, but his son considered his book 'infamous.' It is more than probable that Hill, being a warm personal friend of Lincoln, feared that the publication of the essay would some day interfere with the political advancement of his favorite. At all events, he snatched it out of his hand, and threw it into the fire, from which not a shred escaped."

If that manuscript had not been burned, Lincoln would have become been what he was destined to be — a moral philosopher, the greatest of the American nation. William Seward would have become president in 1860, and won the Civil War in three years. (Lincoln was a terrible Commander-in-chief.)

22:F

Lincoln was an exquisite writer *because* he disbelieved in the Bible as revelation. If the Book of Exodus was a human invention, he could write masterfully, also!

317p
A song sparrow giggles his solo.

341p
It's impossible to imagine Lincoln having sex with his wife, Mary Todd — but it's quite easy to picture him getting a blowjob from one of his aides. While Lincoln doesn't appear "gay" in the contemporary sense, he had an easy masculinity which propelled him towards the company of men.

703p

I've met people who hated Lincoln: Marxists who feel he effected the triumph of capitalism in the USA, anarchists who distrust the power of his state. I understand their arguments, and see their validity. But I can find no other political figure in history with his deep, motherly lovingkindness. He was wracked with a love for the poor — and those even *below* the poor (slaves). Not only that, but Lincoln could articulate these subtle emotions in prose:

> Fondly do we hope—fervently do we pray—that this mighty scourge of war may speedily pass away. Yet, if God wills that it continue, until all the wealth piled by the bondman's two hundred and fifty years of unrequited toil shall be sunk, and until every drop of blood drawn with the lash, shall be paid by another drawn with the sword, as was said three thousand years ago, so still it must be said "the judgments of the Lord, are true and righteous altogether."

23:F

Winnie was taking a shower, and I thought she was talking to herself. Then I realized she was singing. I pressed my ear to the door and heard an old Tony Bennett song: "Who Cares (As Long As You Care for Me)":

> Who cares if the sun cares to fall in the sea?
> Who cares about a bank that failed in Yonkers —
> As long as you've got a kiss that conquers?
> Why should I care?

731p

Suddenly I realize that Grange has stopped saying "paniom."

737p

I saw a hummingbird hovering over our orange nasturtiums in a fierce rain. Maybe hummingbirds beat their wings so fast, they repel rain?

24:F

Lincoln was a Horatio Alger rags-to-riches story, long before Horatio Alger began writing novels.

456p
A tree fell over in the woods behind my house in March, but its buds are opening anyway, just like a drunk who collapses onto the floor of a barroom and continues his conversation, unaware that he's horizontal.

531p
Flipping through *The Psychopathic God: Adolf Hitler* by Robert G. L. Waite, I discovered that when Hitler would flip a coin, he'd always choose "tails." I knew he was a madman, but I didn't know he was *that* perverse!

26:F

What looks like the United States on a map is not one country. It's numerous nations: the Hopi, the Cheyenne, the Navajo, the Iroquois, etc. Each of the Native tribes is officially a separate political entity, like Sweden.

338p
A slanting rain continues.

28:F

In a travel article in the *New York Times* (Friday, May 14, 2010) about the town of Alton, Illinois, I learned that Abraham Lincoln almost fought a duel!

> Just below the plaza lies Alton's grassy riverfront, with a riverboat casino, the Argosy, and a newly constructed outdoor amphitheater. In 1842, on a small island just off the riverbank, James Shields, the Illinois State auditor, and Lincoln were preparing to duel with swords when Shields, apparently frightened by Lincoln's long arms, backed out.

Imagine if Lincoln had died in 1842, pierced by a sword! Why were they dueling?

29:F

A white birch fell over in my backyard last night, with a crash. At least, I assume there was a crash — I didn't hear one. It almost hit the house. In fact, some of the upper branches caromed off the house into the rear garden. Birches have had a blight recently. This one was not old, though dead — less than 40 years of age. I'd been thinking to remove it, but its fall didn't seem so imminent. Also, of course, I hoped it would collapse in the other direction. Three days of rain must have loosened its roots.

How deadly an amiable birch can be! Nature did not plan for us to build expensive houses in her midst.

30:F

According to *A Lincoln Chronology*:

> On September 22, 1842, Senator Shields almost fought a duel with Abraham Lincoln, who had written several letters to a newspaper poking fun at Shields. Lincoln essentially blamed Shields, the Illinois State Auditor, for the financial debt of their state. Recognizing that Lincoln would easily defeat him in a duel, he had his negotiator come to a compromise truce with Lincoln's negotiator at the last minute.

James Shields was later elected Senator of Minnesota, but a court found his election invalid, because he hadn't been an American citizen long enough. (Shields was born in Ireland.) Imagine an Ecuadorian immigrant being elected Senator today!

Is there any country where duels are still fought? With 6 billion people on earth, two of them must be dueling.

506p
I love listening to my wind — the wind circumventing my house.

1:G

Naturally, Lincoln would almost die — by a sword — due to his overactive sense of humor. (Was Abe's choice of a weapon a pun on "swords and Shields"?)

602p
Further research: Shields became the only person in American history to be elected Senator from three states — Illinois, Minnesota and Iowa.

(And Mary Todd, Lincoln's fiancée, helped him write the letters ridiculing Shields, for the *Sangamo Journal*.)

From *Abraham Lincoln: The Prairie Years* by Carl Sandburg:

> Since Shields was the challenger, Lincoln had the privilege of naming the conditions for the contest. He proposed the ludicrous spectacle of a fight with "Cavalry broad swords of the largest size" while standing in a square ten feet wide and about twelve feet deep, which would put the much shorter Shields at a serious disadvantage. Lincoln may have hoped that the silliness (as well as the danger) of the proposed contest would bring Shields to his senses, but both men went ahead with their preparations for the duel until their seconds managed to arrange a peaceable settlement. Lincoln afterwards was embarrassed by the incident and rarely spoke of it.

711p

Winnie is out in her boots, at the compost pile, adding grass clippings, tending the pile's edges.

2:G

History may be viewed most clearly in popular music. Ten years of the Billboard charts are like a century of political history. A singer is crowned king for two years, then abruptly deposed by a former protégé. Four ruling oligarchs divide up their kingdom, then quarrel. An empire is built, then slowly squanders its resources.

Elections exist, also. Fans phone in their votes to radio stations. The People's Choice Awards are a national plebiscite.

Katy Perry is currently the reigning Queen of Pop, but her throne is by no means secure. Already her outlying colonies have begun to revolt.

459p

"The compost pile is now completely aerated," Winnie announced.

4:G

Last night I left my backscratcher out on the kitchen counter! I hope it didn't annoy Winnie. She hates seeing this wooden implement, with its tiny hand.

5:G

At the Sojourner Truth Library I discovered the *Descriptive Catalogue of the Gluck Collection of Manuscripts and Autographs in the Buffalo Public Library*, published July 1899. They had one document from Francis Bacon: a "receipt for money dated June, 1644, given in his capacity of judge of His Majesty's Court of King's Bench." How mysterious is this world! One receipt of the English philosopher reposes (if it still does) in the Buffalo Public Library. What can one learn from gazing at this receipt — how slowly or quickly Bacon wrote an IOU on a particular day in June, 1644? Evidence of his mighty mind, animating his handwriting? And how many Buffalonians visit the library to behold this especial scrap of paper?

404p
Trees shake off rain the same way a dog shakes off bathwater.

7:G

"Local history" is an oxymoron. All history is global. Studying the story of Stone Ridge, the first historical fact is that tribes from Asia moved here.

402p
We all believe that history occurred in the past. In fact, there is only one history, a continuous flow of time which leads to this moment. The problem is how history is taught. We begin with the ancient past and move up to a fairly recent event that textbook writers believe is the last "historical" one. I remember, as a seventh grader, wondering where my history book would end. Would it go beyond World War II? And if so, what story would it tell? Would it discuss Eisenhower, or suburbia?

Has anyone considered teaching history the opposite way — beginning with now, and proceeding backwards? Start with today's newspaper and pursue each story infinitely into the past. For example: "Afghan insurgents packing more objects into bombs": the first news story I read today in *USA Today*. Why are the "insurgents" adding "nails, screws, bolts, metal coils, ball bearings" to their IEDs (improvised explosive devices)? I bet the answer goes back to the 11th century.

456p

I thought I saw a woolly mammoth in the woods today, but when I looked more closely, it was the roots of a fallen tree, caked with soil. From a distance of 70 feet, these once-subterranean organs resemble an extinct shaggy behemoth.

9:G

Grange and I attended "Civil War Days" at the Ashokan Center. Jay Ungar and Molly Mason were performing an instrumental duet at the Pewter Shop, a 19th century-looking room with rustic benches, when we arrived. In a corner I recognized Abraham Lincoln, erect in a tall black hat. Next to him sat Jefferson Davis, the President of the Confederate States of America, in his trademark gray goatee. The two of them eerily resembled a contented married couple. In the back stood the slovenly Ulysses S. Grant. Jay and Molly sang "The Faded Coat of Blue":

> No more the bugle calls the weary one,
> Rest, noble spirits, in their graves unknown;
> For we'll find you and know you among the good and true,
> Where a robe of white is given for a faded coat of blue.

Lincoln sat perfectly still, conscious of the tragic weight on his shoulders.

Unfortunately, after that, Abe spoke. The actor had written his speech himself, and clearly had not studied oratory. His only intelligent line was stolen from Lincoln's speech to Congress in 1848 about his service in the Black Hawk War:

> I had a good many bloody struggles with the mosquitoes,
> and although I never fainted from the loss of blood, I can
> truly say I was often very hungry.

This amusing line captures the boyish foolishness of war.

503p

Talking to the reenactors at "Civil War Days," I noticed their love for the mechanisms of their archaic war: the small white "dog tents," for example, which have buttons on one end, so two tents may be joined together. These canvas shelters are open on both ends. What we forget about the War Between the States is how hot it was. Largely, the fighting was in the South — sometimes the Deep South. There was no Civil War equivalent of freezing at Valley Forge.

709p
Tonight a firefly pressed her round torso against the glass door leading from my deck. She dreamed of entering my house, and telegraphed her yearning in pulses of green light. Though she had the whole sky, she wanted my meager kitchen!

"Go away from here!" I shouted, with cruel directness.

11:G

That Abraham Lincoln impersonator had real talent, when he wasn't speaking. He caught the way Lincoln's body was both erect and bent — which is difficult to convey. And the stillness. He could hold himself without moving for long minutes.

We mistakenly see the past as utterly still, because we know it from photographs and paintings. Probably Andrew Jackson was fidgety, but we picture him stony as a statue.

451p
Both Lincoln and Washington received their military training fighting American Indians. (George Washington was colonel and commander of the Virginia Regiment from 1755 to 1758.) Our primary heroes matured by subduing the rightful owners of this land.

12:G

Today, walking in the woods, I thought I saw a piece of broken glass — but it was just a leaf cupping rainwater.

416p
I find it disconcerting that *People* magazine chooses a "Sexiest Man Alive" yearly, but no one anoints a "Sexiest Woman Alive."

421p
Grange and I saw a crow hop four times on the side of my road — very precise hops, as if he were trying to convey the number 4.

13:G

I moved to the country to live a quiet life, and indeed my life is almost silent. I can hear my heartbeat.

614p
This morning I looked out at my lawn and thought: "There's a new rock, sitting near my wife's herb garden." After a time, I recognized the shape as a brown rabbit, quietly chewing grass. I gave him (or her) the name "The Rational Rabbit."

14:G

Arthur told me that *Esquire* magazine has begun bestowing a "Sexiest Woman Alive" award. Its current recipient is Minka Kelly (chosen partly for her name, I suspect). He showed me a description of Minka on the last page of the October *Esquire*:

> She's beautiful. She's athletic. She's worked gunshot wounds as a surgical nurse. She can act. And you've already fallen in love with her, back when she was a cheerleader. Now fall for her in the November issue...

The "Sexiest Man Alive" is celebrated throughout the media, but the "Sexiest Woman Alive" is only noted by a few horny lawyers.

431p
In the summer, we leave our door open, but on a windy day like today, a breeze will slam the doors to the bedrooms — like an angry teenager storming through the house.

15:G

Once a day, Lincoln would open his office to the public. His hours were 10 AM to 12:30 PM, sometimes stretching till 1:

John Hay, Lincoln's private secretary, wrote that it was "the President's custom [about noon] to order the doors to be opened and all who were waiting to be admitted. The crowd would rush in, thronging the narrow room, and one by one would make their wants known. Some came merely to shake hands, to wish him God-speed; their errand was soon done. Others came asking help or mercy; they usually pressed forward, careless in their pain, as to what ears should overhear their prayer. But there were many who lingered in the rear and leaned against the wall, hoping each to be the last, that they might unfold their schemes for their own advantage or their neighbor's hurt. These were often disconcerted by the President's loud and hearty, 'Well, friend, what can I do for you?' which compelled them to speak, or retire and wait for a more convenient season."

Abe ran his White House like the kooky frontier post office he once managed!

236p
As I walked through the woods, a moth rose up from a spice bush and collided with me — gently.

18:G

A diary is always historical, even if it merely describes the weather. Because the vocabulary for weather changes, slowly but measurably, each decade. (Today we speak of a "weather event," for example.)

19:G

I love history, but I have no desire to be a historian — the same way a Steely Dan fan doesn't wish to write new Steely Dan songs.

441p
The Rational Rabbit reappeared on my front lawn. It stood again by the herb garden, perfectly still except for an occasional quivering ear. Then it leapt into the milkweed.

20:G

I bought *Time* magazine — their Civil War issue. The cover shows a young Abe Lincoln *sans* beard, crying a conspicuous tear. The title is "Why We're Still Fighting the Civil War."

The best part was the photographs by Gregg Segal of Civil War reenactors "at historic battle sites that have been overtaken by modern development." Three soldiers pace dramatically through the Cemetery Hill battlefield, for example, brandishing rifles — next to a Comfort Suites Hotel. In all the photos, you notice the fixed look in the eyes of the soldier-impersonators. Clearly they enter a Higher Reality when they don their uniforms.

The article itself, by David Von Drehle, makes one point and one point only: the war was about slavery. All the pro-Southern arguments about "states rights" are a smokescreen, Von Drehle asserts, correctly. Of course, this being *Time* magazine, he must oversimplify everything:

> The question "What caused the Civil War?" returns 20 million Google hits and a wide array of arguments on Internet comment boards and discussion threads. The Civil War was caused by Northern aggressors invading an independent Southern nation. Or it was caused by high tariffs. Or it was caused by blundering statesmen. Or it was caused by the clash of industrial and agrarian cultures. Or it was caused by fanatics. Or it was caused by the Marxist class struggle.

Of course, all these options are wrong, according to Von Drehle. Especially Marxism, which for *Time* magazine is up there with astrology on the list of silly mumbo-jumbo. Couldn't the Civil War be about slavery and *also* the Marxist class struggle?

Wait, the essay *does* make another point: that the Civil War actually started in Kansas — and was begun by the South:

> It was on May 21, 1856, that a proslavery army, hauling artillery and commanded by U.S. Senator David Rice Atchison of Missouri, laid waste to the antislavery bastion of Lawrence, Kansas. "Boys, this is the happiest day of my life," Atchison declared as his men prepared to teach "the damned abolitionists a Southern lesson that they will remember until the day they die."

This was "Bloody Kansas" — as the state voted whether to be slave or free. John Brown arrived in Kansas with a small band of anti-slavery zealots just too late to defend Lawrence. Three days later, Brown received news that Senator Charles Sumner of Massachusetts had been clubbed nearly to death by South Carolina Congressman Preston Brooks in the Senate, after delivering a powerful speech, "The Crime Against Kansas":

> Brown went "crazy-crazy" at the news, his son reported. That night he led a small group, including four of his sons, to a proslavery settlement on Pottawatomie Creek. Announcing themselves as "the Northern army," Brown's band rousted five men, led them into the darkness and hacked them to death with swords.

(Striking how contemporary that phrase "crazy-crazy" is. You can imagine a teenager in a Techno club saying it.) John Brown's craziness eventually engulfed the entire nation. On one level, wars are begun by anger. We see this clearly with our wars in Iraq and Afghanistan. Soldiers were furious about the attacks of 9/11. Why do young men get so angry? Certainly they themselves don't know why. If they knew, wars would end.

War is, in a sense, the opposite of therapy. A therapist helps you explore why you project your resentments onto others. A war allows you to kill those people.

The photos in the *Time* essay undercut its argument. The Civil War reenactors clearly are not thinking about slavery. Rather, they are entering a drama which makes their lives real. Maybe actual soldiers feel the same way?

21:G

In a review in the *New York Times Book Review* (of *Pops: A Life of Louis Armstrong* by Terry Teachout):

> [Louis] smoked marijuana almost daily for 40 years — it "makes you forget all the bad things that happen to a Negro," he once said...

Much of the beauty of that line comes from the lovely and banished word "Negro."

322p

Does God speak to us through history? It's not impossible. How else would God speak — through angel-messengers?

22:G

I bit into a large Gala apple, but it was rotten, or rather pervasively bruised. Its grainy texture produced a sickly-sweet taste. If I were dying of starvation, I would have gladly consumed it, but I am not, so I threw it away in American disgust.

25:G

History teaches us compassion. All the innocents Alexander The Great slaughtered would be dead today anyway. The dream of empire which drove Alexander seems gentle, almost idealistic, like the songs of The Beatles.

26:G

It's surprising crows don't bury their dead.

442p

Abraham Lincoln was a slut for plays — even as a young man. From *Personal Traits of Abraham Lincoln* by Helen Nicolay:

> Joseph Jefferson, writing of his childhood, tells how in 1839 his father went to Springfield, and relying on the patronage of the legislature, prepared to stay all winter. He built a little wooden theater, but scarcely was it opened, when a revival began in town, and excited church members had the poor little playhouse taxed out of existence. "In the midst of our trouble a young lawyer called upon the management. He had heard of the injustice, and offered, if they would place the matter in his hands, to have the license taken off, declaring that he only desired to see fair play, and would accept no fee, whether he failed or succeeded."

When the matter came to a hearing he made an elaborate argument, covering the history of acting from antiquity down, handling his subject — and his town council — with such skill that the tax was removed. Lincoln was fond of the play, and his championship loses nothing in human interest from the fact that these were probably the first good actors it had been his fortune to see; and that he anticipated a world of delight within its walls if the little wooden theater was allowed to remain.

(Notice the inadvertent pun on "fair play.")

27:G

I have never allowed myself to love butterflies before — they always struck me as girly. But actually, it's the other way around — girls are butterflylike.

356p
More from Helen Nicolay, on the subject of Abe's humorous stories:

Another point is interesting. His stories never varied. He always told them the same way. Once established, the form remained unchanged to the last word and expression.

In this way Abraham was like an actor, reciting his lines.

28:G

I've begun writing historical sonnets:

The Lincoln Douglas Debates: Nearing the End

Stephen Douglas charged that Lincoln held "one
set of principles in the Abolition
counties, and a different and contradictory
set in the other counties." (This in Quincy,
Illinois.) In his rebuttal, Abraham
noted that Douglas admitted his "system

of policy in regard to the
institution of slavery contemplates
that it shall last *forever*." It was October
13, 1858. Douglas wore
himself down, defending the gruesome
torture of human slavery — in Alton,
at the next, and final, debate, his voice
could scarcely be heard, it was so hoarse.

[Notice that it rhymes – or at least "half-rhymes."]

607p
There's a low wind today, massaging the grass.

30:G

My wife is wonderful at thanking me. She touches my arm lightly and looks into my eyes, saying, "Thank you for taking Grange for a walk. I really needed some time." She makes me feel like a racecar driver — a *winning* racecar driver.

453p
I saw the Rational Rabbit again, in the morning, slowly devouring a plantain leaf. He's always in profile; we see his left side.

31:G

"Let's go wait for bears," Grange said to me today.
"Sure," I replied.
We walked out onto our trail, and after a while I asked: "Where shall we sit?"
Grange pointed to a bush and said, "Down here." We crouched beneath the bush, and waited.
"We should be quiet," I whispered.
"Yes. I know," Grange replied, also in a whisper.
It was pleasurable to wait for bears, though I was sure none would arrive. After 15 minutes Grange leaped up and said, slightly louder, "We can go now."
"We didn't see any bears," I pointed out.
"Yes," Grange nodded. "Next time we must try harder."

1:H

I have always loved crows and distrusted robins. Even in my boyhood on Long Island, where crows are scarce, I admired the creatures in cartoons. Heckle and Jeckle were suave, reckless heroes.

While robins hop around so smartly, preening.

351p
Herodotus, the first Western historian, did not publish his books. Rather they were recited aloud to an audience. History was originally a performing art.

406p
I went to drink a glass of water, but a dead moth was floating in it, like an astronaut in space.

2:H

If Lincoln were president today, he'd never be allowed to wear a stovepipe hat. His handlers would say, "Just the opposite, Abe. You want to *deemphasize* your height..." (Lincoln was the tallest president: 6'4".)

416p
Some crows believe they are dogs. This morning a crow barked 23 times in the persona of a Scottish terrier.

454p
Perhaps what is termed "ancestor worship" in tribal cultures is what we call "the study of history."

3:H

My favorite Abraham Lincoln joke: "If this is coffee, please bring me some tea. If this is tea, please bring me some coffee."

359p
The chicory is the tallest I've ever seen it, this year. The leggy weeds are nearly blue-flowered trees.

4:H

Springfield, 1861

The day before Lincoln left for Washington,
he appeared in his old law office, to
discuss business with William Herndon,
his former partner. After talking, Abe threw
himself down on the old backless couch, and
for a while neither spoke. Lincoln seemed to
be remembering the many demands
of lawyering, Circuit Court travels through
Illinois. The conversation resumed.
Abraham stood up to depart, then slowed
at the door, with a change of volume:
"Tell our clients my election makes no
difference. If I live, I'll return here,
to practice law, at the same desk and chair."

According to *Personal Traits of Abraham Lincoln* by Helen Nicolay:

"Give our clients to understand that the election of a
President makes no difference," [Lincoln] said. "If I live
I'm coming back sometime, and will go right on practising
law, as if nothing had happened."

401p
My wife doesn't share my feelings about Lincoln. He's not her hero.
Perhaps my life was deeply influenced by a book my parents gave me: *Meet
Mr. Lincoln.* It may have been the first book compiling the photographs of
Abraham. As a nine year old, I lovingly gazed at his wood-like features.
Lincoln had an exalted sad smile — like Emmett Kelly, the clown.

5:H

On a walk, Winnie picked three bane berries: bright red, about the size
of snow peas.
"These are poison? These will kill you?" I asked.

"Yes," my wife responded.

She placed them on a high shelf, so as not to assassinate Grange.

6:H

Grange and I went out to wait for bears again. This time, he chose a different bush.

Once again, we had no success — except for a rustling nearby, which proved to be a thrush. At that moment, we turned to each other, eyes gleaming!

Some say children should not dictate to parents; when they ask to "wait for bears," you should tell them, "That might be dangerous." But I love the look on Grange's face when he leads me — like a solemn Scottish explorer.

7:H

The "National Briefing" section of the *New York Times* (Saturday, August 7, 2010) contains the headline "Colorado: Bombing Conspirator Sues over Lack of Fiber in Diet." Terry Nichols, who was convicted of conspiracy for the Oklahoma City bombing, has been on three hunger strikes since February. "Mr. Nichols recently filed a handwritten document in a lawsuit filed against the officials at the federal Supermax prison in Florence, Colo., over the lack of whole grains, unpeeled fruit and fewer refined foods in his diet." He said prison officials inserted IVs into his veins to force-feed him.

I had no idea Terry Nichols was so devoted to natural food! It forces me to question my whole view of the Oklahoma City bombing, and of "terrorism" in general.

212p

Driving around today, I noticed how many Tibetan prayer flags there were. Buddhism has quietly conquered my valley.

8:H

Today, at the Sojourner Truth Library, I researched the question: "When did Disco begin?"

The Disco Handbook by J. D. Strong absurdly dates the genre from the Jerry Butler song "Only the Strong Survive" of 1969. *Rockin' Beats* by

Emily Pitner also gives a 1969 date: June 21, to be exact. It was the day of the Stonewall riots, but down the street, at a club called the Haven, a DJ named Francis Grasso played one of his earliest sets. Francis was the first true DJ: a person who plays one continuous stream of music, so that the dancers never pause. (At that time, the B side of a single would often be an instrumental version of the song. Grasso would use two turntables, seamlessly switching from the original hit to the instrumental — thus extending the song for 10 minutes! No one recognized his secret.) In reward for his achievements, Francis dated Liza Minnelli — and lived with Jimi Hendrix's wife after the guitar god's death.

Francis moved to a club called the Sanctuary and continued there until 1972, when it closed. Francis gave up deejaying in 1981, and spent the rest of his life in Brooklyn, occasionally working in construction. He died March 20, 2001, at age 52; Francis was found dead in his apartment by friends. *The New York Times* obituary gave the cause of his death as "unknown, pending results of an autopsy."

A photograph of him from the "late 90s" looks like his face is melting, though his hair is long and black. He appears to be in his 70s. What could destroy a face so quickly? Heroin? Cocaine? Maybe Disco itself is unhealthy. Perhaps dancers *should* stop dancing every three minutes and decide if they need a drink of water. When the "music never stops," the clubgoers never stop. They turn to artificial pills and powders — usually white — to fuel their legs.

I found an interview with Francis Grasso in *The Pop Almanac* and learned:

*He studied literature in college.

*His first career was as a dancer ("a go-go boy") at Trudy Heller's.

*He started dancing because he'd had three debilitating motorcycle accidents; his doctor suggested dancing as therapy.

*He loved being a DJ. ("I would have paid them. I had that much fun.")

*While DJing, he sold Quaaludes. Also pot. Sometimes he would "buy an ounce of speed."

*Jimi Hendrix's wife was crazy. ("Not too stable. But nobody was stable back then.")

*Sometimes, while DJing, he would convince a girl to give him a blowjob by saying: "Bet you can't make me miss a beat!"

*He had his nose broken "about" 12 times. ("Least that's when I stopped counting.")

*He quit DJing because "Everyone was a DJ. Actually, everyone and his mother was a DJ!"

*"See, I really loved the atmosphere; but I couldn't see myself being one of the customers, being on the dancefloor, because I couldn't handle that. I really hate crowds."

Inside a nightclub, the laws of the United States do not apply. It's a "law-free zone." Especially for the DJ. He can sell speed, have his genitals licked, play "Immigrant Song" by Led Zeppelin followed by James Brown's "Hot Pants, Pt. 1"!

9:H

A dead black ant has been clinging to our wall. Grange pointed him out to me, in a corner of the bathroom.

"I didn't know dead ants could still hold onto walls," I told Grange. He nodded.

"What do you want to do with him?" I asked. Grange thought for a moment, then pulled the corpse off the wall and gently placed it in the trashcan. Then he closed his eyes.

"What are you doing?" I asked.

"Saying a prayer," Grange answered.

"What kind of prayer?"

"A big prayer."

10:H

History reduces its characters to caricature, rather quickly. When I was child, people still remembered Winston Churchill as an eloquent speaker and heroic leader. But in *The King's Speech* — which won the Academy award! — Winston was an absurd, cocky alcoholic. History forgets; unless a historian writes a compelling book transforming a cartoon back into a man.

451p

My study of butterflies continues; today I saw my first Monarch of the year. How justly they are named! This creature is larger than any other local Lepidopteran — radiant, royal.

11:H

I am browsing *The Age of Gold: The California Gold Rush and the New American Dream* by H. W. Brands. How fully the Gold Rush influences our thinking about California to this day! Unconsciously, everyone who travels to California hopes to unearth a gold nugget. (In a sense, Hollywood made the Gold Rush permanent.)

406p
I found the carcass of a fawn in the woods: the first I ever saw. The creature was emaciated, still furry. Winnie and I decided not to show the corpse to Grange. The image might haunt him forever.

421p
Carl Jung believed that his depression around 1913 was an augury of the coming world war. Maybe Lincoln's lifetime depression predicted our Civil War?

12:H

Lincoln Returns to Springfield, 1849

"From 1849 to 1854,
both inclusive, practiced law more assiduously
than ever before," Lincoln wrote in the
famous personal sketch five years later.
He had just lost his seat in Congress, and
had to decide where to live. Grant Goodrich
temptingly offered a Chicagoan
job in law, but Abe demurred, writing "it
would kill me" (because he "tended to
consumption"). So he returned to Springfield.
There, Lincoln had time to contemplate. New
plans emerged: the need for study, for real
mental labor. By June, 1860
he'd read Euclid's six books of geometry.

I was shocked that Lincoln, as an adult, read Euclid. Though one senses, in his prose, an advanced mind, and every massive intellect is the result of cultivation.

603p

A hummingbird was flitting around our compost pile this morning — just for a moment, before zooming off. But it would make a good title for a bluegrass song: "Hummingbird in the Compost Pile."

13:H

Lincoln's study of Euclid is more crucial than it seems. The Civil War was ultimately a geometry problem, which Abraham gradually solved. A shape — roughly an X — split into two parts (that's the map of the United States). The question was, how to reunite the pieces?

14:H

I found a *National Geographic* with an ad for a show entitled "Lincoln's Secret Killer?" on the National Geographic Channel:

> The tragic death of Abraham Lincoln is hardly a mystery. What isn't clear, however, is the state of the President's health at the time of his assassination. His gaunt frame and prematurely aged looks have led to speculation that he was gravely ill and possibly dying of cancer. In Lincoln's Secret Killer? diagnosis expert John Sotos sets out to prove it.

703p

It's August, and the songbirds have been silenced by the crickets.

Winnie planted kale this year, and today we ate it for the first time, boiled for an hour: hardy, egalitarian leaves. Very tasty with soy sauce.

16:H

Abraham and Mary Host a Party, February 5, 1862

> The President, in a new swallowtail
> coat, and Mary, wearing a white silk dress
> inscribed with hundreds of black flowers, hailed
> their invited guests: diplomats, judges,
> Senators, Cabinet members — ushered

> along by attendants in mulberry-
> colored outfits, which matched the crockery
> (Solferino). In the background was heard
> the United States Marine Band: its new
> piece, "The Mary Lincoln Polka." Midnight
> came, and the doors to the dining room flew
> open, revealing a weird, dreamlike sight:
> piles of duck, ham, turkey — in the center,
> a model of Fort Sumter made of sugar.

This may be my sharpest sonnet yet. Don't you find the lavishness of this dinner — during a bitter war — troubling? It's a side of Lincoln that's been censored out of history. As McPherson pointed out, he was a rich man, who lived in imposing houses.

17:H

On a website for the Lerner Research Institute at the Cleveland Clinic, I found more info about "Lincoln's Secret Killer":

> Clues ripped from the pages of history books and symptoms spotted in old photographs have led obscure diagnosis expert Dr. John Sotos to compile a compelling medical chart. He believes Lincoln and three of his four sons suffered from MEN 2B, a rare, inherited cancer syndrome... At the Cleveland Clinic's Genomic Medicine Institute, Dr. Charis Eng supervises the first round of DNA testing – from a dress swatch said to be stained with Lincoln's blood.

The essay moves on to describe MEN 2B as "a type of multiple endocrine neoplasia (MEN) caused by RET mutations."

MEN 2B is a pun, like "2B or not 2B." (Or "our love was MEN 2B.")

614p

Do I mythologize Lincoln? Certainly. But he *was* mythic. Abraham led the nation into a vast fratricidal war — a Greek myth multiplied by 500,000. He spent most of his Presidency wondering why the gods had cursed him, like Oedipus. Abraham wrote a note to himself after the Second Battle of Bull Run:

I am almost ready to say... that God wills this contest, and wills that it shall not end yet.

And a few weeks later, Lincoln told an English Quaker that he believed "He permits [the Civil War] for some wise purpose of his own, mysterious and unknown to us."

Lincoln's depression in the White House was partly the sense of being cursed. And his final resolution — "with malice towards none, and charity towards all..." — resembles the wise words of Oedipus at the finale of his tragedy.

703p

It's hard to picture butterflies being ill, but it must happen. I would love to be the first chiropractor to "adjust" butterflies.

18:H

I carry a small notebook. Today while I was shaving, I stopped to write: "KEH X 8." that means I heard a crow say: "keh keh keh keh keh keh keh keh."

344p

The reason Lincoln seems so anomalous a president is that his election was a fluke. It occurred because for one year, America essentially had a parliamentary system. The Democratic Party split in two, and *another* group, the Constitutional Union Party, was formed. Thus Lincoln — an extremely tall, ungainly guy who could barely be described as a politician — was able to win, at the helm of the brand-new Republicans.

506p

The crickets are getting louder every night. They're developing a mob mentality.

19:H

History is the accounting of exceptions. Ordinary people are missing from history books, while unusual ones dominate: Alexander the Great, Benjamin Franklin, Marie Curie. History is crowded with geniuses.

601p

Grange and I lay in the grass this evening watching bats fly. These creatures swoop much differently than birds do. Theirs is *mammalian* flight — nervous and flickering — less direct than robins' paths.

"I want a pet bat," quoth Grange.

714p

It's surprising how few movies have been made about Abraham Lincoln — and even fewer about George Washington. Watching either of these men move through a room makes us nervous. We are comfortable with them on postage stamps.

722p

It's summertime, and unfamiliar people are driving by — some in convertibles! Stone Ridge gets younger in the summer.

20:H

Now that I think of it, there are three types of flight: insect, bird and mammal. The first type is brief and local, usually; the second arclike; the third twitching. (And there's a fourth kind of flight — human. This consists of sitting in a chair, often with a seatbelt.)

306p

Which rock star is most similar to Abraham Lincoln? Definitely Leonard Cohen. (Bob Dylan is nothing like Lincoln — he's much closer to Zachary Taylor.) In fact, if Lincoln lived today he might well be an Orthodox Jew practicing Zen Buddhism, like Mr. Cohen.

321p

Early this morning I thought I heard mice, but it was my wife tiptoeing.

21:H

One of Abraham's mysteries was his extraordinary fashion sense (including a beard, the first of any American Prez). I've never seen him in an ugly outfit. In photographs his clothing is always artfully rumpled like the shirts of the models in *Vogue*. More proof that he was gay?

22:H

Sometimes when Winnie wants to be alone, she'll lie on the bed with two pillows over her head. I saw her with the pillows today.

"What were you thinking about?" I asked her later.

"My job."

307p

There is something absurd about Lincoln's marriage to Mary Todd, beginning with their heights. She was 5'2", he 6'4". The comic motif of a tall person with a short one is ancient. When I was a kid, the comic strip *Mutt and Jeff* still appeared in certain provincial newspapers. Perhaps the most memorable pairing of short and tall is in Shakespeare's *A Midsummer Night's Dream*, where Hermia battles the willowy Helena. Helena calls Hermia a "puppet," and the latter retorts:

> Puppet? why so? ay, that way goes the game.
> Now I perceive that she hath made compare
> Between our statures; she hath urged her height;
> And with her personage, her tall personage,
> Her height, forsooth, she hath prevail'd with him.
> And are you grown so high in his esteem;
> Because I am so dwarfish and so low?
> How low am I, thou painted maypole? speak;
> How low am I? I am not yet so low
> But that my nails can reach unto thine eyes.

It culminates with Lysander shouting to Hermia:

> Get you gone, you dwarf;
> You minimus, of hindering knot-grass made;
> You bead, you acorn.

Abraham and Mary were a maypole and a dwarf. (Is it possible Abe married her as a *joke*?)

Of course, the polarities between Abe and Mary were more than merely physical: she was rich, he impoverished; she was educated, he unschooled.

353p
I asked Winnie why the birds are so quiet in August. "In the spring, they're staking out their territories and mating. Now they have nothing left to say," she replied.

23:H

During the Vietnam War our nation was divided into "hawks" and "doves." That terminology sounds so archaic today, like terms from the 12th century! Nowadays we have no words for those who support the war in Afghanistan, or oppose it.

421p
A swift rain is falling, making a sound like thousands of mouths chewing.

24:H

Lincoln had the least education of any President and was the best writer — proof that schooling wrecks the poetic gift?

456p
Winnie harvested 18 green beans from the garden today – they were sweet as syrup.

26:H

One reason photographs of Abraham Lincoln are so compelling is how early they occur in the history of photography. Seeing photographic documents of him is as incongruous as watching a video of Alexander The Great. The lineaments of Abe's jaw and chin emerged from the forest; they don't belong in a photo. Abe had a dignity that existed before people began "presenting" their faces.

The first president to be photographed was John Quincy Adams, but after his term of office, in 1843. He looked compact and nut-like, glaring out from a rocking chair, his hands clenched together — as if furious at the camera.

The trait that comes through most clearly in Lincoln's photos is his omnipresent humor — his sense of the absurdity of being Abraham Lincoln.

536p

Did Lincoln have a private humor — one he only shared with close pals? Richard Nixon would call up Bob Hope and beg him for racist jokes. Did Lincoln enjoy that kind of comedy? (It's not impossible.) Or did he joke about the war dead when no one could hear?

28:H

Today I'm watching the wind, in the form of undulant willow fronds.

407p

Lincoln Moves to Springfield (1837)

On April 15, Lincoln rode into
Springfield on a borrowed horse, all his
possessions in two saddlebags. He drew
up to the general store, A. Y. Ellis
& Co., and asked the price of a
mattress, sheets and a pillow. Joshua
Speed, one of the owners, reckoned the cost
as $17. "That is doubtless
fair, but I have not so much money," Abe
replied. "I am here to try an experiment
as a lawyer." Speed, who had seen Lincoln
give a speech, impulsively offered a
deal: to share his own room, and double bed,
with Abe. "Where is your room?" Lincoln said.

The room was upstairs, and what Speed actually said was: "I have a large room with a double bed up-stairs, which you are very welcome to share with me."

Was he in love with Abe?

When Speed pointed to the winding stairs that led from the store to the second floor, Lincoln picked up his saddlebags and ascended. Shortly afterward he returned beaming with pleasure and announced, "Well, Speed, I am moved!"

(That's from *Lincoln* by David Herbert Donald.)

I know "experiment" is not a perfect rhyme for "Lincoln," but it makes an key point, subliminally: that Lincoln *was* an experiment, within the experiment of the American Republic.

The last line has only nine syllables, to indicate the speed with which Abe embraced Speed. They lived together almost four years.

458p
Today I sat in the woods, closing my eyes to better interrogate the silence. After a few minutes, I opened my eyelids to see a red fox speeding past, not twenty feet away — in mid-leap.

29:H

George Washington was infatuated with war. One reason he became our first commander was that he appeared at the Continental Congress in full military uniform — the only uniform at the gathering. But Lincoln, who presided over our most devastating war, had no stomach for fighting. He hated even hunting. Abraham spoke of his service in the Black Hawk War with irony and embarrassment. And he opposed the popular — and entirely imperialistic — Mexican War. A "wannabe warrior" birthed our nation, but a brooding pacifist brought us to maturity.

511p
Today in Stone Ridge I came upon a large number of people — maybe twelve — gathered around a guy of 23 in red shorts and a t-shirt juggling three rubber balls. A tall woman pointed a camera at him. I asked a woman with a sharp nose and an iPod, "Is this a movie shoot?"

"No, it's a photography shoot."

"What's it for?"

"Fruit of the Loom."

30:H

My friend Rex The Mystic told me: "Every tree is a soul: the former soul of a living person. But not the part we see; the real soul lives underground." Rex learned this from a Native American wise man.

417p
Do crows have nests? If so, I imagine them filled with cigarettes, ashtrays and posters of The Ramones.

603p
At the local vegetable stand, I bought two hot peppers that literally resemble parts of the Devil's anatomy — his horns. They are bright red, maliciously curved.

31:H

Rereading this journal, I am embarrassed how unserious it is: summaries of comic books, facts from the *New York Times Book Review*, amateur sonnets.

But history *is* a collection of fragments. The jumble in an antique shop — paintings without titles, greenish vases, aging photographs, a book with a half-illegible name inscribed, slightly moldy quilts — that's history, before it's been domesticated by historians.

434p
Besides, my first exposure to history was in comic books. As a kid, I owned the *Classics Illustrated* biography of Lincoln, and also one for Teddy Roosevelt. I read them over and over, but only remember one anecdote from each. They are: 1) When Lincoln was a boy, he told his brother to muddy his feet, then Abe picked him up and held him upside down. The brother made tracks on the ceiling, and when their mother returned, they claimed a stranger had entered, walking on the ceiling. 2) Teddy Roosevelt was shot by an assassin, but didn't die, because he happened to have a lucky silver dollar in his pocket!

507p
Watching a small, gray, manic moth today in the backyard was exhausting. There are millions of birdwatchers, but are there "mothwatchers"? Can anyone tell moths apart?

1:I

Suddenly I remember another story from *Classics Illustrated*: Lincoln's greatest speech. This oration was so brilliant that all the reporters were dumbstruck — they took no notes. Thus the speech is entirely unrecorded. Is this true?

1106a

Grange and I were walking along our road when we heard a loud sound. Looking up, we saw a truck pulling a horse van. Suddenly we were staring at the asses of two horses, both with long tails. One was tan, one brown. This was as unexpected as a hooded cobra.

722p

For decades, clocks in jewelry stores were always set to the time that Lincoln died: 7:22. (I guess not in the South, though.) As if our nation came to a halt, eternally, with Abraham's killing.

Does anyone still follow this practice?

2:I

I found this in the *Lincoln Reader*:

Abraham Lincoln's "Lost Speech" was delivered on May 29, 1856, in Bloomington, Illinois. Tradition states that the text was lost because Lincoln's powerful oration mesmerized every person in attendance. Reporters laid down their pencils, forgetting to take notes. This address is believed to have been an impassioned condemnation of slavery. It is possible the text was deliberately "lost" owing to its controversial content. Lincoln gave the speech at an Anti-Nebraska convention in Bloomington that culminated with the founding of the state Republican Party.

William Herndon asserted that some of Lincoln's House Divided Speech was not based on new concepts at the time of its delivery. He wrote that Lincoln's "house divided against itself cannot stand" originated with the famous Bloomington speech of 1856.

Though it was known as the Lost Speech, its content influenced people nonetheless. Those who heard it were often asked to paraphrase it, and a frenzied group of supporters spearheaded Lincoln's drive toward a second place finish among U.S. vice presidential candidates in 1856.

3:I

In the meadow behind the house, a purple flower has proliferated. I must ask Winnie its name. I can learn the identity of a flower 36 times, and forget each time. I never remember flowers, because they don't remind me of anything else.

317p

I asked my wife. They're asters.

324p

I'm paging through *Abraham Lincoln: An Illustrated History of His Life and Times*, published by *Time* magazine in the magic year 2009 (bicentennial of Abe's birth). Lincoln's life was a steady progression from rural to urban. Each time he moved, it was to a larger town. Abraham began at Sinking Spring Farm in central Kentucky and ended his life in the nation's capitol.

Also, his work became more and more abstract — starting with physical labor and ending with the subtle tasks of a Chief Executive. In a sense, Lincoln's life was a symbol of the American nation, progressing from rural to urban, from labor to "Communications." (Nowadays, every college student I meet majors in Communications.)

415p

This morning I saw a small green worm hanging from an invisible thread, in midair, writhing in agony or delight.

619p

Lincoln became famous for his oratory rather than his deeds. His "House Divided" speech and debates with Douglas brought him attention. Abraham was a thinker, not an administrator.

4:I

The big mystery of Lincoln: why did he fail to act after his election? He adopted a strategy of invisibility, in Springfield, fueling the South's paranoia. If he had reassured the South, "I won't end slavery," the Civil War may have been averted. Through inaction, Abraham brought on the bloodbath.

611p
Honey is a thermometer. You can gauge the temperature by how much it's crystallized.

615p
Grange and I saw the horse couple again, speeding by in their trailer. Somehow they look married.

653p
The *Time* book lists Abraham's literary tastes, which I'd never seen before. His favorite Shakespeare play was *Macbeth*; he loved Edgar Allen Poe, and had memorized "The Raven." But he despised novels! Or as the text (written by a committee) states: "He was immune to the leisurely attractions of fiction, apparently; an early attempt to read Walter Scott was a failure." Instead, he admired Robert Burns.

Which makes sense. A man who loved novels could not have written:

> Four score and seven years ago our fathers brought forth on this continent, a new nation, conceived in Liberty, and dedicated to the proposition that all men are created equal.

Clearly was composed by a man who grew up reading:

> And the Lord said unto Moses, Depart, and go up hence, thou and the people which thou has brought up out of the land of Egypt, unto the land which I sware unto Abraham, to Isaac, and to Jacob, saying, Unto thy seed will I give it.

5:I

As Grange and I walked on the road, an elderly English couple approached us. "Excuse me," said the man, "do you live around here?"

"Yes," I replied.

"May I speak with you?"

"Yes," I replied, and stopped walking. Grange halted next to me. The man came slightly closer. "Are there wild animals around here?" he asked.

I smiled. "There are black bear," I answered, "and a few deer. Let's see, there are rabbits. Snakes. Skunks. Minks."

"We don't have skunks in England," the man ventured.

"You have hedgehogs!" I replied. He smiled proudly. "Have you been to England?" he asked.

"Just once, in 1991," I answered, then continued with my list: "We have mountain lions, and bobcats — but you see them very rarely."

At that point the woman looked up at me. "Are there leopards?" she asked, her eyes glittering.

"No, we don't have leopards," I chuckled.

"Well, we must be getting on," remarked the man. And the two of them ambled past us. Their speech was full of wonderful English hesitations. They never told me their names.

6:I

This morning the wind blew open the kitchen door and spun the ceiling fan six times. A ghost-wind!

615p

Studying *Macbeth* may have helped Lincoln defeat the Confederacy. Robert E. Lee had a touch of the doomed Scot in him. If Lee had fought a defensive war like George Washington, he might have prevailed, but an arrogant pride insisted he attack Gettysburg. Like Macbeth, he wasn't satisfied with one murder; he had to continue until he destroyed himself. From Shakespeare, Abraham knew Lee's weakness.

7:I

This morning a light, apologetic rain fell.

354p

Reading the *Illustrated History* — or rather, gazing at its large photographs — I am immersed in the Wooden World of 19th century America. Everything was composed of dead trees: boats, rafts, houses, the pipes men smoked. The world was much more *solid* before plastic.

601p

Only one photograph survives of Abraham's father; also one of his stepmother. Even the poor wished to be photographed by the 1860s. (Both pictures are undated.) Abe's real mother, Nancy Hanks, slipped out of this world without a graven image.

The photo of Thomas, Abraham's father, shows a deeply conflicted man, resembling Clark Gable with a harelip. Also, Thomas looks nothing like his son. In fact, there is a tradition that Abraham was an illegitimate child:

"After Abe's birth a man by the name of Abraham Enloe living in this region claimed him as his son. Thomas Lincoln and Enloe had a regular set-to fight about the matter, in which encounter Lincoln bit off the end of Enloe's nose. Finally, Lincoln, to clear himself of Enloe, moved to Indiana. As back as I can remember there lived in Hardin County three families of Enloe's, all from North Carolina and all said to be cousins. Isham Enloe married a widow Larue and had a family of some distinction. Abe Enloe, another cousin, tall, dignified-looking man of fine personal appearance, very neat, silent, and reserved; more of a bookworm than anything else; married a Vernon — one of our best families — and was the father of a respectable family. Then comes our veritable Abe Enloe who claims to be the father of Lincoln. He was over six feet high and a fine specimen of physical manhood. I remember him with part of his nose bit off as one of the institutions of the county for thirty years. Very silent, very unobtrusive, never drunk nor boisterous, he seemed not to suffer in reputation by the conduct of his sisters who were more or less boisterous. I never had much to say to him except when I happened to sell him some article for his farm in my uncle's store. He may have been a man of destiny also and patiently filled the place assigned him by Providence."

That's from *The Real Lincoln: A Portrait* by Jesse W. Weik (Houghton Mifflin, Boston, 1922). Weik is quoting from a letter by "a man who lived in Elizabethtown, a member of one of the leading families and a lawyer."

Bit off his nose! Paging Dr. Freud! Thomas Lincoln, Abe's father, was saying: "You are a big tall, sexual man who cuckolded me! I *would* bite off your dick, but I can't reach it, so I'll settle for your nose!"

And isn't it odd that Lincoln has the same first name as his supposed father? Did the scheming Nancy Hanks quietly arrange this?

8:I

Grange and I saw a white Ford pickup truck pull up to a stream; two men emerged and started hauling big rocks into the truck. We watched from a distance, but I didn't approach them. What can one say? There's no law against stealing rocks.

341p
Lincoln was an Oedipal guy. He despised his father, and adored his two mothers: the saintly Sarah Bush Johnston Lincoln and the vanished Nancy Hanks. Lincoln biographer David Herbert Donald observes: "In all of his published writings, and indeed, even in reports of hundreds of stories and conversations, he had not one favorable word to say about his father."
No wonder Abraham was depressed! And he was born 97 years before psychoanalysis!

347p
As Grange and I walked along the road, he found an old hair tie on the ground, picked it up, and started twisting it around. I don't worry about germs, unless he's eating a lollipop that fell in dogshit. I watched my son happily pull the red elastic.

603p
Did you know that Abe's mother was not the only one to die of "the milk sick"? Her two cousins, Thomas and Elizabeth Sparrow, who were living with the Lincolns at the time, also perished. It's difficult to believe a cow can eat snakeroot and murder, with her milk, three strong adults.

9:I

In her photo, Lincoln's stepmom looks like a male comedian playing The World's Kindliest Mother.

417p
I can easily picture Lincoln standing in the center of a room, intoning:

> Presently my soul grew stronger; hesitating then no longer,
> "Sir," said I, "or Madam, truly your forgiveness I implore;

But the fact is I was napping, and so gently you came rapping,
And so faintly you came tapping, tapping at my chamber door,
That I scarce was sure I heard you" — here I opened
   wide the door; —
Darkness there, and nothing more.

10:I

Grange and I sat by the stream in the woods, watching five water bugs. Each would sit on the surface of the water, perfectly still, then suddenly push off, as if she had jets on her heels.

456p
Illiterate parents, a mother who died young, not much food, a struggle to survive — Abraham Lincoln lived like a kid in a ghetto. Except for the pine trees, his cabin could have been a room in East New York or the South Side of Chicago.

503p
My favorite flower, the chicory, is still in bloom, clinging to the shoulders of highways. The petals darken as the year lengthens — now almost purple.

11:I

The county lawnmower came down our road today, with an aggressive roar. It looks like a tractor — the bluest tractor I've ever seen. The mower moves quite slowly, and shaves down the grass and weeds on the side of the road. "Grange would love this," I thought, but he was regretfully napping.

652p
Has anyone ever painted a portrait of Lincoln as black? If an African-American didn't, you would think a racist would. I imagine Lincoln glorious in black skin.

12:I

My wife was eating a banana with a spoon this evening. "What are you doing?" I asked.

"I thought it might be fun," she answered. She had peeled the banana, and was slowly spooning it into her mouth. "I saw someone do it in a movie once," Winnie explained.

"What movie?"

"*Witness.*"

752p

I lay in bed, watching flashes of celestial light, accompanied by booming sounds — as if vandals were blowing up Rosendale.

13:I

Winnie and I must have a fairly peaceful relationship, because it's been years since either of us slammed a door.

14:I

Lincoln referred to his condition as "the hypo" (short for "hypochondria," the contemporary name for depression). Little did Abe know that 100 years hence, heroin addicts would use that term for their beloved hypodermic needles.

723p

Everyone should read about the Filipino struggle for independence from our nation, after the Spanish-American war. Most Americans believe we were never defeated in war until Vietnam, because textbooks edit out our defeats. I like to talk about the War of 1812, the guerrilla war in the Philippines. People should know that their nation was defeated, but not destroyed. Americans are unnecessarily terrified of defeat.

15:I

Grange and I found one of those mylar balloons, deflated, in the woods. It was six colors — magenta, orange, yellow, blue, red, white — with the inscription: "Hey, Kid, It's Your Birthday!" Grange was fascinated with it, and seemed to believe that it had grown there.

402p

Lincoln began cultivating a beard in the midst of his Presidential campaign. It's hard to imagine that happening today — John McCain sprouting a Van Dyke in mid-election.

407p

I hate to drink hot liquids. When a friend offers me a cup of tea, I always say yes. Then I nurse the cup, waiting for the tea to cool. By the time the liquid has cooled, I've forgotten about it. I travel through the world leaving a trail of tepid teacups.

16:I

Abraham had one of the most self-created intellects of all time. He thrived on being teacherless. He was like a self-taught painter — an "outsider" president.

17:I

Grange and I have begun picking trash up from the road, as we walk. (Actually, this was his idea.) Today we found an old foil wrapper for "Nature Valley Crunchy Granola Bars — Maple Brown Sugar." Grange carried the wrapper in his hand, depositing it in the kitchen trash.

18:I

Lincoln was a cautious, moderate politician who was cast by Fate in the role of a revolutionary. Ultimately, he destroyed a system of human bondage that had flourished for centuries — a system he personally despised. I wish Fate would use me for a high purpose, but so far, She is unwilling.

452p

On our walk, Grange and I found a wild apple tree, and after much deliberation, chose three apples from the grass: small fruits, a third the size of a normal Macintosh. But the markings are much more elegant — red striations on a greenish field, like canvases by Monet.

But how will they taste?

19:I

The Black Hawk War, in which Lincoln "fought," was named after a person, not a tribe! Black Hawk was a charismatic chieftain who attacked the U.S. with the British in the War of 1812. Using the phrase "The Black Hawk War" would be like calling World War II "The Hitler War."

307p
Ants clearly have no fear of death. They're like ancient Spartans.

652p
All three of us ate the little apples. They had a tight, sweet, cashew-like flavor — if you ate around the brown spots. We all liked them, but Winnie was most enthused: "I could eat one every morning!"

20:I

New Salem is a key place for Lincoln. He spent six years there in his 20s, becoming a postmaster, militia officer, election clerk, storekeeper, surveyor, state legislator. But the town flourished for only four of those years — and was founded the year before he arrived, in 1830! New Salem arose like a cloud and vanished like a cloud — as if the Lord created it to educate Abraham.

456p
As soon as Grange and I stepped onto the trail behind our house, five squirrels darted out from behind a tree, and quickly scattered. Did we interrupt a secret squirrel conclave?

507p
One reason new Lincolns don't arise now is that everyone works too hard. Back in the 1830s, you could split a couple rails, then lean on a stump and read Pliny for 15 minutes. They don't let you do that at Wal-Mart.

646p
Today, for the first time in my life, I looked at two butterflies and thought, "They must be mother and daughter!"

21:I

Lincoln had a natural, rugged beauty. It was unnecessary to carve his face into a mountain, because a mountain was already carved into his face.

416p

If Lincoln reincarnated after his death, who would he become? If he were going to be another President (which seems doubtful), the first eligible option was Warren G. Harding, who was born November 2, 1865. My guess is that Abraham reincarnated as a writer. Maybe Gertrude Stein? She was born February 3, 1874. Consider these two passages, the first by Abraham, the second by Gertrude:

> Certainly there is no contending against the Will of God; but still there is some difficulty in ascertaining, and applying it, to particular cases. For instance we will suppose the Rev. Dr. Ross has a slave named Sambo, and the question is "Is it the Will of God that Sambo shall remain a slave, or be set free?" The Almighty gives no audible answer to the question, and his revelation—the Bible—gives none—or, at most, none but such as admits of a squabble, as to its meaning. No one thinks of asking Sambo's opinion on it.

> Considering the circumstances there is no occasion for a reduction, considering that there is no pealing there is no occasion for an obligation, considering that there is no outrage there is no necessity for any reparation, considering that there is no particle sodden there is no occasion for deliberation. Considering everything and which way the turn is tending, considering everything why is there no restraint, considering everything what makes the place settle and the plate distinguish some specialties. The whole thing is not understood and this is not strange considering that there is no education, this is not strange because having that certainty does show the difference in cutting, it shows that when there is turning there is no distress.

22:I

Lincoln became a politician because he needed the money! The store he founded at New Salem with William F. Berry had failed, and he owed $650, which was a lot of moolah in 1833. (Actually he owed half of that, but Berry suddenly died, and Abraham assumed his partner's debt.) Abe was a smart, likable guy — and tall — so why not be a politician?

451p
It just occurred to me — did Berry, burdened by debt, kill himself?

454p
According to a Berry family genealogy website, William Franklin Berry died at the age of 24 — two days after his birthday! He had no children. They give no cause of death.

503p
No wonder New Salem fell into decline! It was named after a cursed town in Massachusetts, site of the evil witch trials! "New Salem" was a karmically misbegotten name.

519p
Another reason Lincoln ran for the state assembly: politics is accessible in a small town. I have considered it myself — campaigning for a judgeship.

602p
Grange and I walked in the gentle rain, then stopped to examine an acorn's cap, which had fallen off its "head." The cap lay on the road, upside down.
The inside of the cap was unpredictably yellow.

650p
Lincoln's inner life is a perpetual conundrum. It's difficult not to project one's own spiritual beliefs onto him. Julia Mygatt Powell wrote in *Flashlights of Abraham Lincoln* (Angelus, 1921):

> Mr. Lincoln was a Christian mystic. Francis Grierson, in
> his little book called "The Practical Mystic," approaches
> the truth most nearly.

Mr. Lincoln said himself to Mrs. Rankin:

"I cannot, without mental reservation, assent to long and complicated creeds and catechisms. If the church would ask simply for the Saviour's statement of the Substance of the Law: 'Thou shalt love the Lord thy God with all thy heart, and with all thy soul, and with all thy mind, and thy neighbor as thyself,' that church I would gladly unite with."

In Springfield, Abraham was considered a freethinker, even an atheist. It's known that he would ridicule the Bible to his friends, but so might a Sufi. Certainly, Lincoln used Biblical imagery once he was president, but what choice did he have? Could he quote from the Zoroastrian scriptures? Were Lincoln's religious allusions just literary devices — or mystic intuitions? No one knows.

23:I

Stone Ridge has become noticeably swanky since we moved here. When people ask, "Where do you live?" and I reply, their eyes widen with suspicion and awe. True, we inhabit the least fashionable corner of town, but that doesn't matter. A town's reputation ennobles or degrades its citizens.

642p

Reading transcripts of the Lincoln-Douglas debates, what's most impressive is how Abraham transformed his merciless personal hatred of slavery into precise argument — the sublimation of anger into articulate logic.

And what is the ultimate source of Lincoln's anger? Probably his father. The only two things Abe despised were human bondage and his dad.

651p

My wife says those acorn caps are pried off by squirrels. They can eat the acorn-meat but not the little "hats."

24:I

Lincoln stopped being a politician so he could make *more* money! He figured, "Why not be a wealthy lawyer?" He wanted to be more than a petty state legislator.

641p

Lincoln's position on slavery was completely irrational. He despised it, bitterly opposed its spread to other states, but didn't want to abolish it. In Peoria, he mightily declared, "A house divided cannot stand," but what does that mean? That the South must free its slaves? That the North must allow slavecatchers everywhere? Abraham did not — and could not — explain.

656p

According to this illustrated history, Lincoln's stepmother Sarah — the one who encouraged his education — was herself illiterate. This is not exactly a contradiction, but it's poignant.

25:I

Here is an excerpt from Francis Grierson's *Abraham Lincoln: The Practical Mystic* (John Lane, 1918). The scene is a backwoods revival meeting in Spring Creek, Illinois on August 13, 1837. The speaker is Peter Akers, superintendent of the Ebenezer Manual Labor School, a Methodist seminary:

> "I am not a prophet," [Akers] said, "but a student of the Prophets; American slavery will come to an end in some near decade, I think in the sixties." These words caused a profound sensation. In their excitement thousands surged about the preacher, but when at last he cried out: "Who can tell but that the man who shall lead us through this strife may be standing in this presence," a solemn stillness fell over the assembly. There, not more than thirty feet away, stood the lank figure of Lincoln, with his pensive face, a prophet as yet uninspired, a leader as yet unannounced. The preacher's words had fallen like a mystical baptism on the head of this obscure pioneer, as yet unanointed by the sacrificial fire of the coming national tragedy.

26:I

A bear shit in our backyard last night: a brown pile, the size of a five year old's baseball cap. "He was eating apples," Winnie diagnosed, examining the bear scat.

441p

Later, walking into town, I saw a similar, larger mound of feces, probably authored by the same bear. Bears make shit-detectives of us all.

458p

Lincoln had an acute historical sense, evident in his foremost writings. He took a long, evolutionary view of human events. American democracy is a fragile system, Abraham knew. Its success is not inevitable; it must be nurtured. And he saw slavery within the grand sweep of history. He knew that in two generations we'd look back at this "peculiar institution" with guilt and horror.

Lincoln's historical wisdom extended to his prose. Like his contemporary Emily Dickinson (of whom he was ignorant) Abe wrote deceptively simple, undecorated sentences destined to be enshrined a century hence.

27:I

One reason wars are periodic is that warmongers must wait a generation for memories of the last slaughter to fade. The Civil War made the U.S. a pacifist nation for 33 years — and the Spanish-American War was so brief and painless, it was barely a war. From the Civil War to World War I was 49 years.

709p

I thought the chicory was all gone, but Grange and I found two plants today, gleaming like the hard blue eyes of an 82-year-old sculptor.

28:I

Here is a quote from Black Hawk (in *A Treasury of American Quotations*):

> Courage is not afraid to weep, and she is not afraid to pray,
> even when she is not sure who she is praying to.

351p

My wife has bought a new, uglier bag of potatoes. I quote from the text of the bag:

US No. 1 Grade
CAVENDISH
Produce

Russet
BAKING
Potatoes

2.27 kg (5 LB)
Product of CANADA

But the imagery is weak: a photograph of two near-identical potatoes posed on a rumpled tablecloth, with a dull green background. Photography is ruining potato bag art.

29:I

After the first Battle of Bull Run, according to the *Illustrated Lincoln*, the South could have captured Washington. *Then* what would have happened? Would the entire nation have been ruled by the Confederacy? Would the Southerners have instituted Reconstruction in reverse — racism decreed by law? Would Lincoln have been beheaded?

431p
Flies are feasting on the bear scat.

30:I

Mary Todd dated Stephen Douglas before she met Lincoln. In fact, he was her suitor. The original Lincoln-Douglas debate was in Mary's mind.

1:J

Lincoln and Douglas only debated eight times! I never realized their debates were so few (though amplified by the mass media of the time — newspapers).

507p

Grange and I found an exotic lizard on the road: glinty black, with yellow specks like stars in a night sky. The creature stood completely still, though we saw its lungs breathing. The tip of its tail was missing.

2:J

Now is true Fall: that is to say, leaves are falling from the trees. Grange and I have a new goal: to catch a leaf before it reaches the ground. It's surprisingly tricky. So far we've come close, but caught nothing.

423p

The last words of John Wilkes Booth are different in the *Illustrated History*:

> ... Booth opted for what he hoped would be a heroic last stand: he remained inside while his pursuers set fire to the barn and then shot him through the neck. "Tell Mother I died for my country," he said to the soldiers, then looked down at his now paralyzed hands and muttered "useless, useless" before dying.

To refresh your memory, Rick Geary's comic book had: "Tell my mother that I die for my country... I did what I thought was best..." Perhaps one cannot rely on graphic novels for historical accuracy.

443p

Now I've looked up Booth's death scene in *The Lincoln Assassination Reader*:

> In his dying moments, he reportedly whispered, "Tell my mother I died for my country." Asking that his hands be raised to his face so he could see them, Booth uttered his last words, "Useless, useless," and died as dawn was breaking.

Notice here "Mother" has become "my mother." Of course, no one knows for certain what "Useless, useless" means. Was Booth referring to his paralyzed hands? Or did he mean the assassination? Or his own life?

I read Adam Gopnik's *Angels and Ages*, a dual biography of Lincoln and Charles Darwin, both born the same day. The book takes its title from the uncertainty about Edwin Stanton's words when Lincoln died. Did he say, "Now he belongs to the ages," or "Now he belongs to the angels"? Dozens of people were packed into a tight room in a boarding house; some heard each version. The same uncertainty accompanied the death of John Wilkes Booth.

And what about Lincoln's last words? Everyone who dies has last words, even if they're unintentional. One never hears Lincoln's last words cited. They were probably: "That gal is a real firecracker!" — a comment on *Our American Cousin* (the play he was watching).

3:J

I'm wrong. Lincoln's last words are recorded, by Carl James Flaghorn, in *Lincoln: A Complete Biography*:

> Several other people were invited to join them, until finally Major Henry Rathbone and his fiancée Clara Harris (daughter of New York Senator Ira Harris) accepted.
>
> The Lincoln party arrived late and settled into the Presidential Box, which was actually two corner box seats with the dividing wall between them removed. Mrs. Lincoln whispered to her husband, who was holding her hand, "What will Miss Harris think of my hanging on to you so?" The president replied, "She won't think anything about it". Those were the last words ever spoken by Abraham Lincoln. It was about 10:15 p.m.

"She won't think anything about it": simple, American last words (especially the slightly redundant "anything.") And politically astute, shrewdly assessing the social environment. Clara Harris did *not* disapprove of Abraham and Mary holding hands. If anything, she was likely touched.

Politicians are paid to know what others are thinking, and skilled politicians are usually correct. Lincoln understood that most people don't obsess on the President holding hands; they're thinking, "Does this dress look too tight on me?" Everyone worries about themselves. That's what Abe's last words mean.

451p

Today is another rainy day — a day to stay inside. That's why Grange and I went out, to defy the Conventional Mind. Walking in our ponchos, we felt brave. Several wet leaves fell around us, but we caught none.

4:J

History is governed by physics. Lincoln, for example, was bound by the Law of Gravity. In fact, when he ordered the largest mass execution in U.S. history, Abraham was collaborating with gravity. (Thirty-eight Sioux warriors were hanged after fighting American soldiers in the Minnesota River Valley in 1862.)

501p

One reason Reconstruction was so brutal was John Wilkes Booth. He tried to kill the whole ruling elite of the U.S.! No wonder the North was unsympathetic to the plight of the former Confederacy!

603p

Cats and dogs avoid rain, but raccoons love a wet, chilly night.

5:J

Here's why Lincoln's funeral train made so many geographically odd stops: it replicated the path he took to Washington! This may have been the first "funeral train" in history, which is fitting, because Abraham was a lawyer for the railroads, presided over the transcontinental railway — Lincoln trusted in railroads.

And remember, the locomotive was a recent invention. A funeral train must have struck people as an oxymoron, like a funerary iPod seems to us.

446p

The key act in the Lincoln assassination was Booth jumping off the balcony shouting, "Sic semper tyrannis!" (or possibly "The South is avenged!") and immediately breaking his leg. Booth had been trained as an actor, not a gymnast. If you hurl yourself from a balcony, you'll hurt yourself. But John Wilkes saw himself as a superhero (before the concept existed) capable of any physical feat. The balcony-leap displays Booth's magical thinking.

451p
A brisk wind rushes through the valley casting leaves off trees, like a madman gleefully pulling out the hair of passing children.

6:J

I was wrong about funeral trains. The first one was in England on November 7, 1854. Victorians loved funerals. They didn't fear death like present-day Americans. If Victorians had built rockets, they would have quickly developed the "funeral blastoff."

413p
Lincoln was a Southerner. He was born in rural Kentucky, and lived there until he was seven. (Jefferson Davis was also a Kentuckian.) He married a woman from Lexington, Kentucky. Historians note with admiration that Lincoln never castigated the South. And three days before he died, on April 11, after Lee had surrendered, Lincoln spoke from the second-floor window of the White House, then asked the band to play "Dixie" — calling it "one of the best tunes I have ever heard." (John Wilkes Booth was watching.)

It's quite possible Lincoln considered himself Southern. What he hated was slavery, not the South. The Civil War was a battle between two Southerners.

416p
Walking on the lawn, I saw not a snake but the *movement* of a snake — wriggling grasses.

7:J

I finished the *Illustrated History*, which has a bewildering finale: photographs of Fidel Castro and Khrushchev at the Lincoln Memorial (plus, of course, Martin Luther King — though it oddly fails to mention that the March on Washington was the 100th anniversary of the Emancipation Proclamation). Castro looks penitent before the godlike statue of Abraham.

This is the chapter on Lincoln's legacy, entitled "Lincoln in the American Memory." *Time* magazine's implication: "Abraham Lincoln was the *true* revolutionary; these Communists are imposters."

356p
It's been lightly raining, which has pulled down the yellow birch leaves. This morning my car was festooned with ovals, like a cupcake covered with sprinkles.

8:J

Grange found a McDonald's cup on the road, next to a straw. On the cup was written:

ENJOY

and on the reverse:

WHERE MMMM
MEETS AHHH

Ever notice how our french fries
prime your taste buds for an icy
cold gulp of your favorite
beverage? And vice versa?

I'm lovin' it

What is the purpose of these cup-messages? To establish intimacy with the McDonald's customer? (The cup seems to be *chatting* with you.)

731p
Grange and I rushed after numerous falling leaves – catching none of them.

9:J

Of all the 43 American presidents, only one had "Honest" in his nickname. That's a bad sign. No one ever called Coolidge "Honest Calvin."

414p
In October the air is so clear, you feel like your vision's improving.

441p
Lincoln is remembered as a tragedian, but lived the life of a comedian. The *Illustrated History* refers to his "seemingly limitless stock" of jokes — which he loved to laugh at himself, bent over double.

Many funnymen are depressive. Lincoln's melancholy may have been the natural temperament of a jokester.

513p
Dew has colors, the same way stars in the heavens do: faint but discernible hues. Today's dew was bluish.

10:J

Though Lincoln never drank liquor, the *Illustrated History* has the tavern license he registered for in New Salem, when he ran a shop with William F. Berry:

> Business was slow, so they applied for a liquor license, though Lincoln's signature on the application may not be in his hand, suggesting the profligate Berry may have forged it. In later years, Lincoln the politician would be haunted by the charge that he had been a tavern keeper, costing him the votes of teetotalers. Much later, when prohibitionists claimed Lincoln as one of their own, barkeeps across America hung up framed copies of his liquor license.

Lincoln's inconsistent stance on alcohol — he didn't drink it, but would sell it, because people enjoy it — mirrored his position on slavery. He disbelieved in slavery, yet allowed others to practice it.

11:J

Grange and I found an empty half-gallon Tropicana orange juice container by the road. Who chugs juice, then throws the container out the window? Methodists on a spree?

356p
Lincoln's literary reputation rests on a narrow base: two short speeches, the Gettysburg Address and the Second Inaugural. He always wrote elegantly, but very little of his prose is quotable. Many of his oft-quoted lines like "You can fool some of the people all of the time, and all of the people some of the time, but you can't fool all of the people all of the time" are inauthentic.

401p
The youngest soldier in the Civil War was 10, the oldest 73, I learned from the book *Do Fish Drink Water?: Puzzling and Improbable Questions and Answers* by Bill McLain.

12:J

Grange and I are still pursuing our autumn "sport": attempting to catch a falling leaf. We scooted after dozens today and caught zero.

456p
One of the big questions I am struggling with is: "When exactly did Lincoln grow his beard?" We know that he was inspired by an 11-year-old girl named Grace Bedell who wrote him a letter on October 15, 1860. But did he have a beard by Election Day? How long did it take to produce his whiskers?

In *Lincoln* by David Herbert Donald, I found an unprecedented photo — Abraham with half a beard! The date was November 25, the place Chicago. But was Election Day early in November in the 1860s? I have a vague memory that Election Day moved in the 19th century.

It seems crucial that our first bearded president grew his facial hair in response to a girl. (Lincoln himself had four boys, no daughter.) Truly great men heed the words of little girls.

607p
At a rest stop on the New York Thruway, I found a calendar (actually a "Town Planner") for the municipality of Howell, New Jersey. The bottom of each page is a row of discount coupons:

$100 OFF
WHITENING

107

With One Hour
In Office Visit
ZOOM!
(Regular $600)
SMILE CENTER
OF HOWELL

Most striking are the names of the visiting teams at the high school: the Kannapolis Intimidators, the Greensboro Grasshoppers, the Charleston RiverDogs, the Delmarva Shorebirds, the Hagerstown Suns, the Augusta GreenJackets, the Hickory Crawdads. The names of American high school teams are high poetry, remnants of the 19th century. (What exactly is a "Smile Center"?)

13:J

Lincoln and the Bible

Lincoln's parents were Baptists; the only
time his father grew furious at him
was when Abraham mocked the long, wildly
impassioned sermon of a preacher, limbs
flailing. But that didn't stop Honest Abe,
who continued to doubt Christian dogma.
Thomas Paine's *The Age of Reason* was a
beloved work, and quietly he gave
voice to misgivings about Christ's godhood.
Still, Abraham loved the Bible, keeping
a copy on his desk always. Could
he avoid imitating its rhythms? "*Giving*
freedom to the *slave*, we *assure* freedom
to the *free*," Lincoln wrote, after Antietam.

14:J

Today we had six blackouts, one lasting 12 seconds.

451p
Election Day in 1860 was Tuesday, November 6. Lincoln didn't campaign before the election, so no one knew he was growing a beard. Americans thought they were electing a clean-shaven "Rail-Splitter." (The campaign literature I've seen makes Lincoln look considerably younger than he was.)

Lincoln won 39.8% of the popular vote. Is that the smallest winning percentage in history?

15:J

No. It was the second smallest. The first was John Quincy Adams in 1824, with 30.9%.

502p
Every time I see a butterfly, I believe in a happy future. Emily Dickinson wrote: "Hope is the thing with feathers," but I say: "Hope is the thing with chitinous wings."

16:J

Lincoln met Grace Bedell, at the Westfield, New York train station, as he rode toward Washington after the election. He kissed her! According to the *New York World* of February 19, 1861:

> Mr. Lincoln stooped down and kissed the child, and talked with her for some minutes. Her advice had not been thrown away upon the rugged chieftain. A beard of several months' growth covers (perhaps adorns) the lower part of his face. The young girl's peachy cheek must have been tickled with a stiff whisker, for the growth of which she was herself responsible.

417p
"It's supposed to rain for the next ten days," Winnie said.

17:J

Grace Bedell later recounted her memory of meeting Lincoln:

> "He climbed down and sat down with me on the edge of
> the station platform," she recalled. "'Gracie,' he said, 'look
> at my whiskers. I have been growing them for you.' Then
> he kissed me. I never saw him again."

Grace married George Newton Billings, a Union veteran, moved to Delphos, Kansas, and died there in 1936.

Isn't it strange that Lincoln kissed her? Or is that just the 19th century style? One can't imagine Washington leaning over with his walrus-bone teeth, to nuzzle little Gracie.

502p
Neither Grange nor I have caught a leaf yet. He came quite close — within three feet — and almost ran into a ditch. Grange wisely turned back at the last moment.

"Just stand under a tree and wait for the wind to blow," advised Winnie, but that's harder than it sounds. Waiting for a breeze is like waiting for a cement truck. One doesn't always arrive.

And we're running out of leaves! Suddenly the trees are nearly depleted.

18:J

There's a Grace Bedell Foundation! I found its website. Apparently this group is responding to the threat towards Grace's house, which is on the list of "Most Endangered Historical Sites in Kansas." A statue was erected of Grace in Delphos in 1966! (How fitting that she chose to live in that town, named after the oracle in Greece. Grace herself functioned as an oracle for Abraham.)

342p
Today, on the banks of the stream, Grange and I saw a large yellow butterfly flying east — not fluttering, flying like a bird. We exchanged a look. You never see a butterfly *hurrying*.

356p

John Wilkes Booth invented anarchism, unintentionally. Thirteen years after Booth's crime, Max Hödel attempted to assassinate Kaiser Wilhelm of Germany, the first anarchist "propaganda by deed." (Was Hödel inspired by Booth?)

19:J

"When I was a kid, the girls would chant:

> Lincoln, Lincoln,
> I've been thinkin',
> What the heck
> Have you been drinkin'?
> Is it whiskey?
> Is it wine?
> Oh my God,
> It's turpentine!

while they were jumping rope," Winnie told me.

459p

Most Americans feel pride in Lincoln. Abe grew up in a world of bullies and fools; he had to fight to be sublime. And he succeeded! Lincoln began as a (failed) shopkeeper in New Salem, Illinois, and grew noble, eternal and wise. Abraham's greatness was an American improvisation.

21:J

I had a dream last night that Grange collapsed in my arms. He might have been dying. As he swooned, he said: "I never eat my food, not at all."

I woke up in fright. "Perhaps he has never eaten his food," I wondered, half-awake. "Have I ever seen him, for certain, swallow a mouthful?"

358p

Abraham Lincoln: An Illustrated History of His Life and Times constantly overpowered me. Written anonymously, but with key essays from pop historians — the smartest being "Across the Great Divide: The friendship between Lincoln and Frederick Douglass required from both a change of heart" by John Stauffer — this book finds obscure archival photos: for example, did you know that throughout Lincoln's presidency the U.S. Capitol building was incomplete? How symbolical! A photo circa 1846 shows the temporary dome, built (I guess) to keep out the rain. Another amazing discovery: Elizabeth Keckly, Mary Todd Lincoln's "modiste" (fashion advisor) and dressmaker. "Keckly was a former slave whose father was her wealthy white owner; she endured years of physical and sexual abuse at the hands of white masters before managing to buy her freedom in 1855, thanks to her expertise as a dressmaker and enterprise as a businesswoman." She was a "daily presence in the White House"! Elizabeth Keckly appears in a long and satiny gown (photographically).

The introductory essay, "The True Lincoln," by Joshua Wolf Shenk, who wrote "the acclaimed 2005 bestseller, *Lincoln's Melancholy*," goes around in circles, dueling with the many misinterpretations of Lincoln, but becomes fixated on the gay hypothesis put forth by C. A. Tripp in *The Intimate World of Abraham Lincoln*:

> Tripp's claim proceeds from what Jonathan Ned Katz calls "epistemological hubris and ontological chutzpah." A scholar of 19th century sexuality, Katz explains that the terms homosexual and heterosexual did not exist in Lincoln's time, and that fact is just one piece of evidence that the concepts of gender, sexuality and same-sex relationships were radically different in Lincoln's world. In those days, men could be openly affectionate with one another, physically and verbally, without having to stake their identity on it.

Yes, but did Joshua Speed and Lincoln have sex during the three and 3/4 years they slept together?

22:J

The *Illustrated History* displays the only ugly photo of Lincoln I have ever seen:

> The portrait at left, a rare image of Lincoln in a white suit rather than his usual dark garb, was taken in 1858, only hours after Lincoln won his most famous law case.

Lincoln was defending William (Duff) Armstrong, the son of an old friend from New Salem, who was charged with being an accessory in a murder trial.

Lincoln looks young, thoughtful, with jug ears — but the bright white suit is entirely nauseating. It resembles a straitjacket.

417p
Grange and I went for a walk today. We both stopped suddenly, seeing a branch that had fallen from a red oak. There was a clean break; the way it lay on the brown leaves was troubling. Never before had I noticed how much a branch is like an arm (hence the word "limb").

503p
The *Illustrated History* has the first war photograph ever taken, of American troops in Saltillo during the Mexican War. They are on horseback, with long coats and anvil-shaped hats. A black dog looks on from the right, entirely unimpressed. The whole thing is out of focus and vaguely resembles Picasso's drawings of Don Quixote.

23:J

Mary Todd Lincoln held séances in the White House, to converse with her dead son Willie. What did Lincoln think of these occult rituals? Did he believe Mary was batshit crazy? Or did he maintain an open mind? Like most successful marriages, Abe and Mary each represented the repressed side of the other. Lincoln was modest and self-effacing, Mary bold and decisive. Abraham was rational, Mary credulous.

407p
Grange and I gazed up at the stars last night. "Why are there so many stars?" he asked.
"God made one, and when She saw how easy it was, She made lots of them," I replied.
About half the time, I use the feminine pronoun for God.

603p
Without a doubt, Lincoln began the relatively brief vogue for bearded presidents. The encroachment of facial hair started with John Quincy

Adams, and in fact Lincoln's beard was the negative space within Adams' muttonchops. After Abraham, the beards grew progressively fuller, from Grant to Rutherford B. Hayes — then vanished forever.

25:J

"Lincoln" is a pun — the participle of the verb "to link" — and Lincoln *was* linkin' together the states of the union. That pun is employed subliminally in the name of a toy I had as a child: "Lincoln Logs." A round can contained small wooden spars, with slots fitting together to form a miniature log cabin. Do they still exist? I'm not sure.

536p
Grange and I did more leaf-chasing today, to no avail. It's not easy to catch one of these falling tree-pennants!

26:J

Yes, Lincoln Logs are still for sale (plus a devious imitation called "Frontier Logs.") A "Little Prairie Farmhouse" in pink appears to be directed towards girls. Conversely, for the more militaristic there is "Fort Lincoln" (172 pieces).

615p
More and more, I find myself focusing on the question, "What did Lincoln do during the 1860 election?" Did he keep his day job? Did he subtly direct his campaign? Was he formulating plans for his administration?

And when did candidates start campaigning for president? When did they stop just sitting around being too high-minded to beg for votes? Which election was that?

27:J

"Did you feel the earthquake?" Winnie asked, walking in the house today.

"No," I replied cautiously. She had been in the village, at the library, and distinctly felt the world shake. So did Ginny, the librarian.

Whoever heard of a Stone Ridge earthquake?

28:J

According to the *Lincoln Reader*:

> Before 1860 "people saw candidates in the flesh less often than they saw a perfect rainbow." Lincoln followed the longstanding tradition of almost every presidential candidate since George Washington. During his front porch campaign, Lincoln made no new speeches and did not leave his hometown of Springfield, Illinois. Although he met with hundreds of visitors, Lincoln answered all political questions by advising listeners to read his published speeches, such as those from the debates with Douglas in 1858; even an August crowd of 30,000 that marched in a parade eight miles long in front of his home failed to cause Lincoln to speak more than a few words.

And the first presidential candidate ever to "stump" during the election was none other than Stephen Douglas, in 1860! He gave speeches and interviews, North and South!

419p
A new theory: Lincoln chose to free the slaves by proclamation, rather than by a Congressional bill, because he wished to *write* the decree. That's how much he loved writing. (Unfortunately, the document is not memorable as prose.)

452p
I saw a yellow butterfly flying up as a brown leaf flew down. We are approaching the end of the Lepidopteran season, no doubt. The long butterflyless winter soon commences.

29:J

Extreme tallness is itself a type of sadness. The phrase "it's lonely at the top" is literal as well as metaphoric. And true of Abraham.

358p
Lincoln had an obsession with slavery. He returned to politics in 1856 to battle human servitude. Abraham is unlike every other American politician, in this way — his work grew out of a single moral compulsion.

30:J

One more anecdote from the *Illustrated History*: Lincoln once told a congressman: "Doesn't it strike you as queer that I, who couldn't cut the head off a chicken, and who was sick at the sight of blood, should be cast into the middle of a great war, with blood flowing all about me?"

31:J

This morning a rainstorm arrived abruptly, with nearby warlike thunder. A few minutes before the deluge, crows wildly cried behind my house, broadcasting their fear.

321p
Lincoln by David Herbert Donald gives four theories for Abraham's depression. The first is nightmares.

> Henry Clay Whitney, who began traveling Judge Davis's circuit after 1854, reported that Lincoln was afflicted by nightmares. One night, when they were sharing a room, Whitney woke to see his companion "sitting up in bed, his figure dimly visible by the ghostly firelight, talking the wildest and most incoherent nonsense all to himself." "A stranger to Lincoln would have supposed he had suddenly gone insane," Whitney added. Awaking suddenly, Lincoln jumped out of bed, "put some wood on the fire, and then sat in front of it, moodily, dejectedly, in a most somber and gloomy spell, till the breakfast bell rang."

The next three theories are by Herndon: domestic unhappiness, chronic constipation and the "blue-mass pills" Lincoln took to relieve his constipation.
Why was Abraham unable to shit? My guess is that his diet was deficient in fresh produce and that he didn't drink enough water. He was tall! He should have been ladling water all day.

What are "blue-mass pills"?

1:K

Grange and I came upon a black leaf, on the road — an oak leaf almost entirely blackened. (Did it have a disease?) I'd never seen such a botanical oddity. A "goth" leaf!

407p
From *Studies in 19th-Century Medicine* by Mark Drelfus:

> According to Robert Perlman from the University of Chicago Medical Center, the blue-mass pills contained mercury, licorice root, rose water, honey, sugar and rose petals — an appealing mixture if you don't know mercury is a poison. Perlman says they were prescribed for hypochondriasis (now called depression), not constipation. "A study published in the Summer 2001 issue of *Perspectives in Biology and Medicine* reformulates a common anti-depressive medication of the nineteenth century and shows that it would have delivered a daily dose of mercury exceeding the current Environmental Protection Agency safety standard by nearly 9000 times."
>
> "Mercury poisoning certainly could explain Lincoln's known neurological symptoms: insomnia, tremor and the rage attacks," said Robert G. Feldman, M.D., professor of neurology, pharmacology, and environmental health at the Boston University Schools of Medicine and Public Health, an expert on heavy metal poisoning. "But what is even more important, because the behavioral effects of mercury poisoning may be reversible, it also explains the composure for which he was famous during his tenure as president."
>
> Lincoln stopped taking the "blue-mass pills" in 1861, a few months after his inauguration, because they made him "cross," writes Perlman.

Says the Royal Society of Chemistry:

Blue Mass, sometimes known as "Blue Pills", was used widely, often ineffectively, for a range of 19th century ailments, including toothache, constipation, childbirth pains, parasitic infestation and tuberculosis.

This is the first I've heard of Lincoln's towering rages. Apparently they only occurred in the 1850s. While president, he was renowned for stoic patience.

2:K

Grange and I walked in the Stone Ridge Cemetery. I wrote down the name of one deceased man: Urijah Temple (1843–77). He died when he was 34, like Charlie Parker. In the 19th century, Americans had memorable names: Featherstone, Hall, and Cease. (It's chilling to see a headstone with the word CEASE on it.) Before Italians and Poles came here, names were usually meaningful English words.

Grange and I waited in a grove of maple trees for leaves to fall. We'd watch a quivering leaf, but the quivering leaves never descend.

Gravity was quite strong today. We'd see a leaf dropping, but by the time we raced towards it, the earth had it. One fell right through my hands! A leaf can swoop and twist four times a second!

Finally, Grange was under one, and grabbed it before it could reach the ground. He succeeded! Grange saved that leaf — a small maple — in his jacket pocket. Later, he showed it to Winnie — and to anyone who would look.

322p

Immediately after the discussion of Lincoln's melancholia, Donald moves on to his attempt to become a famous lecturer, during an era when Americans flocked to speeches (public speakers):

His most ambitious and curious effort was what he called "a sort of lecture" entitled "Discoveries and Inventions," which he first read to the Young Men's Association in Bloomington on April 6, 1858. The first half was Lincoln's version of the history of discoveries, ranging from Adam's invention of the fig-leaf apron in the Garden of Eden to the steam engine. The second half dealt with the invention of writing and printing — together with the discovery of America, the introduction of patent laws, and what Lincoln called, oddly enough, "the invention of negroes, or, of the present mode of using them." It was a commonplace production, resting on a few articles in the *Encyclopedia Americana* and on Old Testament references to such subjects as spinning and weaving. Over the next 12 months Lincoln delivered this lecture in several Illinois towns, but, though by this time he was a possible presidential candidate, it attracted only small and unenthusiastic audiences. It was, as Herndon said, "a lifeless thing — a dull dead thing, 'died a bornin [sic].'"

As much evidence as there is of Lincoln's greatness, there is just as much of Lincoln's ordinariness. He was a fairly typical person made majestic by the crucible of suffering. William Herndon, who knew him well, was obsessed with this thesis. He was compelled to write his biography to show that heroism is a choice, not the gift of a distant deity.

3:K

This morning a small bird was inside our willow tree. I say "inside" because the tree is rather small: 27 feet high. The drooping branches form a kind of birdcage. As I walked near the tree, the creature began to shout: "Behhh! Behhh! Behhhh!" — almost like a crying baby.

451p
Wasn't it stupid for John Wilkes Booth to kill Lincoln on Good Friday? If he wanted to obliterate Abraham entirely, he certainly chose the wrong day.

4:K

Was Lincoln circumcised?

514p
Grange and I agree that catching one leaf is enough for the season. Still, we'd like to catch a second, just for fun. Our new "sport" has completely changed autumn.

6:K

Lincoln's assassination was a scene from a melodrama, the stealthy heroic killer — with only one bullet in his pistol! — sneaking up behind the President, under cover of the audience's laughter. It seems like a play written by an actor, which it was.

346p
A light rain is falling — what I call a "beginner's rain."

357p
Religion was more radical in the 19th century; major denominations attacked slavery. The equivalent today would be the Presbyterians denouncing capitalism.

9:K

The First Draft of the Gettysburg Address

The summer of 1863, there
was a lull in the war. Mary returned
from her vacation in the mountains, cheered.
She and the President felt they had earned
the right to attend the theater; they saw
Maggie Mitchell in *Fanchon, The Cricket.*
Then came the news of two victories: at
Vicksburg and Gettysburg. Abe spoke to a
band of serenaders at the White House.
How fitting that this good news appeared
on the Fourth of July, Abraham mused.
"How long ago is it? — eighty odd years
since for the first time a nation assembled
& declared 'all men are created equal'."

I shortened the quotation from *Lincoln* to make it sonnet-like. The original is: "How long ago is it? — eighty odd years — since on the Fourth of July for the first time in the history of the world a nation by its representatives, assembled and declared as a self-evident truth that 'all men are created equal'." I inserted the ampersand to lessen the syllable-count.

452p
Now the leaves have mostly fallen. It's a yellow year — almost no reds or oranges — though the leaves at my feet display many variations of yellowness, some spotted with little brown dots. The warm weather this autumn is probably to blame. It takes cold to squeeze out brighter colors.

10:K

I can imagine an alternate history where Lincoln was brain-damaged after Booth's assault and spent the next 30 years smilingly sitting in a chair, cured of his hypochondriasis. Most melancholy is caused, ultimately, by too much thinking.

454p
The South did not embrace John Wilkes Booth because he violated their code of honor. After Robert E. Lee so gracefully surrendered, like a true gentleman, Booth's act appeared cheap and vengeful. Besides, what good would it do to kill the president? The Yankees would only replace him with another, worse president!

11:K

"Let us make holes," Grange said today. We walked outside and he picked up a stick as a tool. Then he began digging, next to a patch of dandelions. I found a smaller stick, and dug next to him. Grange was quiet, determined. He unearthed a small grey rock and threw it over his shoulder. Then he continued digging. After 20 minutes, Grange surveyed his hole, which was about 6 inches wide. "This is my hole," he said. I nodded.

652p
Is there a bumper sticker asking: WWLD? ("What Would Lincoln Do?") And how *would* Lincoln respond to our current political crisis? One — perhaps evasive — answer is: "He would learn." Throughout his life, Lincoln grew, as a politician and a man. That's what's most noble about him. The book *Our Lincoln* takes this as its central theme. Two examples are his military conduct of the Civil War and his position on race. It's easy to say, "Lincoln was a racist" — and quite true — but really one must say, "Lincoln was an *absolute* racist in 1846, and much less so by 1863." The story of Abraham's friendship with Frederick Douglass is the tale of a man overcoming a lifetime of ignorance.

One reason Lincoln always kept learning was that he had no formal education — or anyway, less than a year's worth. School provides a beginning and ending to study. In the first 12 years, you learn the basics, then you specialize, develop a skill. Afterwards, you go forth and practice that skill. But how could Lincoln ever be done with education, when he never started?

703p
Most of the leaves have fallen by now, but today a gust of wind pulled down dozens, at once, in front of our house. Leaves slip through the atmosphere like kids sliding down a spiral staircase.

12:K

Reading excerpts from Carl Sandburg in *A Treasury of American Folklore*, I learn that my favorite Lincoln joke is apocryphal. Lincoln became a hero of folklore — perhaps even before his death — like Nasruddin, the funny Sufi philosopher who lived in 13th century Turkey. (In fact, some of the same jokes were attributed to both of them!) As Sandburg writes:

> Little folk tales and snatches of odd wisdom known to common people of the ancient kingdoms of the Persians and the Arabians, came to be known among the common people of the farming districts in Illinois, hitched up somehow to Abe Lincoln.

Under that category is the remark: "Say, if this is coffee, then please bring me some tea, but if this is tea, please bring me some coffee." Lincoln and Nasruddin are both holy fools, who easily outwit judges and kings.

506p
Edward Everett giving a two-hour speech at Gettysburg, followed by the simple, stunning Gettysburg Address, is like a Zen teaching story.

13:K

Today Grange dug four holes, all fairly close together. Then he counted them. He is learning numbers.

327p

In a section of *A Treasury of American Folklore* entitled "Patron Saints" (devoted to George Washington, Lincoln and Johnny Appleseed) the editor, B.A. Botkin, writes this enigmatic sentence about Abe:

> He is also the perfect exemplar of the Freudian formula which sees in his homeliness the potentiality of our own impotence and of the American democratic creed of the self-made man. ("Any boy can become President.")

"The potentiality of our own impotence" doesn't mean that we have the potential to become impotent, but rather that our current impotence masks an untapped potential. But why "Freudian"? Because Lincoln is so tall? He's a giant phallic symbol?

601p

My old friend Eric Foner reviews *The American Crucible: Slavery, Emancipation and Human Rights* by Robin Blackburn in *The Nation*. Here's what I learned: by the mid-19th century, every nation had abolished slavery except Cuba, Brazil, and the United States. Slavery persisted in Cuba until the 1870s and only ended in Brazil in 1888. But the ex-slaves fared worst in our nation: "The blacks of the U. S. South gained the least from the ending of slavery." It's as if the Southerners, after long arguing that emancipation would worsen the lives of African-Americans, set out to prove it true. Today Brazil is a large, multiethnic nation with a socialist-leaning government, Cuba is Communist and anti-racist, and the American South is a bulwark of half-crazed Christianity and reactionary bitterness.

14:K

Brown leaves follow us into the house, clutching our pants legs. Leaves prefer the warmth of home to the chilly woods.

412p

I wonder if Lincoln's melancholia was partly a crisis of social class. As a youth, he was never described as sad — just goofy, eager and driven. As an adult he became a type we see still in the U.S.: a man who has abandoned his origins, never speaks of his childhood, and through persistent hard work (and maybe a shrewd marriage) gains a tenuous hold on wealth. But in his large house, he feels empty. He's lost his fundamental identity.

421p
Birds eat insects – until they die. Then insects eat birds.

15:K

Today Grange and I dug six more holes: three apiece. We're still using sticks as tools, but we each have a "chosen stick" that we save next to the house.

457p
Lincoln was forced to mythologize himself because in his time there were two types of people: those who stayed put and those who pushed on. The former were known to the same village their whole lives, but the latter were forced to create a "backstory" for themselves — a story that could never be authenticated. From *Huckleberry Finn*.

> The king got out an old ratty deck of cards after breakfast, and him and the duke played seven-up a while, five cents a game. Then they got tired of it, and allowed they would "lay out a campaign," as they called it. The duke went down into his carpetbag, and fetched up a lot of little printed bills and read them out loud. One bill said, "The celebrated Dr. Armand de Montalban, of Paris," would "lecture on the Science of Phrenology" at such and such a place, on the blank day of blank, at ten cents admission, and "furnish charts of character at twenty-five cents apiece." The duke said that was him. In another bill he was the "world-renowned Shakespearian tragedian, Garrick the Younger, of Drury Lane, London." In other bills he had a lot of other names and done other wonderful things, like finding water and gold with a "divining-rod," "dissipating witch spells," and so on.

In 19th century America, once you left your home you could be anyone – like Lincoln in New Salem.

16:K

I'm reading *Lincoln: The Biography of a Writer* by Fred Kaplan. A writer's biography must begin as a reader's biography, and we know the exact copies of certain books Abraham read as a child. Kaplan makes much of Thomas Dilworth's *New Guide to the English Tongue*, generally referred to as *Dilworth's Speller*. The edition Abe's mother had was published in Philadelphia in 1747, by Benjamin Franklin! Lincoln was born in 1809. Abraham's *Speller* predated the revolution — by 30 years! People kept books for 70 years back then, as if they were ancestral jewels.

According to Kaplan, both of Lincoln's mothers were literate, though Nancy couldn't write.

And Lincoln was an excellent speller! Who would have guessed? In 1818, when he was nine, a schoolmate recalled: "We had spelling matches frequently. Abe was ahead of all the classes he Ever was in." Abraham seems to have taught himself largely by repetition and memorization. Often he read books aloud. Lincoln said: "My mind is like a piece of steel, very hard to scratch anything on it and almost impossible after you get it there to rub it out."

Among his earliest writings — which do not survive — were epigrams protesting cruelty to animals. (No one can publicly suggest that Lincoln's feelings towards animals were related to his compassion towards African-Americans. It's a dangerous subject, to this day, though it's quite possible that Lincoln saw blacks as similar to sheep and goats.)

Kaplan almost suggests that Dilworth inspired Lincoln's melancholy, with verses like:

> Ah! Few and full of sorrow are the days
> Of miserable man: his life decays
> Like that frail flower, which with the sun's uprise
> Her bud unfolds, and in the evening dies...

Do books make us sad? Certainly, illiterate people seem happier. Reading the Great Writers, one learns that most of human life is disappointment. Looking around you, as the illiterate do, most people seem fairly content. And I was wrong about Abe's cheerful youth:

> His eyes, later observers remarked, were filled with sadness even early in his life.

writes Kaplan. No doubt from reading tragical poetry like "Elegy Written in a Country Church-Yard"!

17:K

The fallen leaves on the ground are now slowly crumbling. Complete leaves are few. (What crumbles them? The wind? Raccoons walking over them at night?)

526p

Lincoln read novels as a kid! Only later did he turn against them. He loved *Robinson Crusoe* and *Pilgrims Progress* (if you count the latter as a novel). Plus *The Arabian Nights*.

Having so few books in the house is really helpful to a young writer. I always felt intimidated by my parents' bookcases. But Lincoln had two volumes: the Bible and good old Dilworth, which he could diligently master — until his father remarried, when he was 11, and his second mother brought a load of books. By then, Abraham was ready for a new influx of literature: Daniel Defoe, Noah Webster's *Speller*, Lindley Murray's *The English Reader*, William Scott's *Lessons in Elocution*.

Lincoln was literate in a largely book-free world. He began writing letters for neighbors, and witnessing legal documents. He became a postmaster! He ran for the state legislature. Just being a lover of reading set him apart. Lincoln's life emerged from books. He was the rebuttal to Mao Tse-Tung's dictum that "Political power grows out of the barrel of a gun." For Abraham, power emerged from the pages of an anthology.

18:K

A man named William Kimmig sent me this quote in an e-mail:

> "I see in the near future a crisis approaching that unnerves me and causes me to tremble for the safety of my country; corporations have been enthroned, an era of corruption in High Places will follow, and the Money Power of the country will endeavor to prolong its reign by working upon the prejudices of the People, until the wealth is aggregated in a few hands, and the Republic destroyed. "
> — Abraham Lincoln

I sensed that it was a fraud, but I was surprised (reading *Remnants of Lincoln*) how old it was. This quote appeared 30 years after Lincoln's death, early enough for his secretary, Nikolay, to denounce it as inauthentic. But this "quotation" is a skillful hoax. It sounds like Abraham, complete with archaic capital letters, and it mimics well his prophetic power. (Though in reality, Lincoln was quite sympathetic to corporations.)

19:K

I never noticed this before, but the 4" high maple saplings *also* experience autumn. Their leaves turn yellow, but cling longer than the leaves of their parents. It's late November, and they still haven't made the 3 1/2" journey to the ground.

507p
Kaplan gives a small compendium of Lincoln's dirty jokes. Here's one:

> "In the morning after My Marriage," Christopher C. Brown told William Herndon, "Lincoln met me and Said — 'Brown why is a woman like a barrel —' C.C.B. could not answer. Well Said Lincoln — you have to raise the hoops before you put the head in."

But almost none of his jokes were transcribed:

> "Lincoln... had been telling his yarns... A farmer Said — Lincoln why do you not write up your stories and put them in a book.' Lincoln drew himself up — fixed his face, as if a thousand dead carcusses... were shooting all their stench into his nostrils, and said 'Such a book would Stink like 1000 privies.'"

according to "friend and colleague" Henry Whitney.

20:K

Grange and I are still making our excavations. We've been going back to the same spot in the woods, and elaborating our holes into two curving trenches.

536p

The Civil War was caused by Manifest Destiny, the belief that the United States should reach the Pacific Ocean. If the 13 colonies had never expanded, no war would have come. Manifest Destiny was an evil, much like slavery. It was, in a sense, the enslavement of the continent.

During the Colonial period, Virginia claimed all land due west, extending to the Pacific. Imagine if that boundary had remained intact! Virginia would be the only state on earth 3000 miles wide.

21:K

What was the meaning of Lincoln's scatological humor? I've been pondering this for days, then it hit me: his constipation! Unable to actually shit, he was forced to be a "potty mouth"! Lincoln's jokes were a symbolical bowel movement.

22:K

Lincoln in 1859

Abe's speechifying tour of Iowa,
Ohio, Wisconsin, Indiana
and Kansas, in 1859, led
the *Illinois Gazette* (which few men read)
to propose Lincoln for President — the
first newspaper ever to do so. Abraham
himself doubted he was fit even
to be Senator (or so he told a
journalist in '58) though Mary
believed he would someday be Prez. "Just
think," Abraham would say, about to burst
with laughter, "of such a sucker as me
as president!" Then his comrades and he
would shake and roar with unrestrained glee.

23:K

Grange and I have been back at our digging. Our two trenches today met!

327p

Lincoln believed the world was only 6000 years old (unlike his birthday-mate, Charles Darwin)! Or at least he did in November 1839, when he made a philosophical speech defending the National Bank:

> Again, we all feel to know that we have to die. How? We have never died yet. We know it, because we know, or at least think we know, that of all the beings, just like ourselves, who have been coming into the world for six thousand years, not one is now living who was here two hundred years ago.

Or did Abraham just *pretend* to believe in the Biblical account of history? Abraham Lincoln and Emily Dickinson, besides being contemporaries with rhyming names, had very similar theological stances. Both are perched between cynicism and mysticism, in regards to the Great Beyond. With Abe & Emily, you never know when they're joking about religion and when they're confessing deep faith.

24:K

One area where Lincoln was ahead of his time was as a father. His children dominated him almost exactly the way kids intimidate American parents today. (Visitors to the White House were sometimes hosed by the prankish Tad.) As a politician, Abraham was prophetic but not visionary, yet one may call him without exaggeration an avant-garde parent.

517p

In November, the sun gets brighter in the forest, because the leaves no longer obscure it. I never noticed this before, and I'm 48 years old! (But then I never spent so much time in the woods digging holes.)

25:K

I am up to the excruciating romantic section of Kaplan's book. Lincoln was vividly aware of how ugly he was — a quality we can no longer see. Like the iconic Hollywood actors — Humphrey Bogart, Katherine

Hepburn, Bette Davis — Lincoln was a funny-looking person who taught us, through the power of his character, to admire his face.

28:K

Today, while putting away the silverware, I found a spoon in the fork slot. I've never seen that before. I guess our household is quite orderly.

419p
Lincoln served just one term as Congressman. During his tenure, he vigorously attacked the Mexican War, which was highly popular — and already over! (Americans, then as now, loved short, vainglorious, successful conquests.) Kaplan ties himself in knots trying to prove narrow political calculation in Lincoln's acts, but it's hard not to believe Abraham was motivated by morality. Did he know of Thoreau, the other noted dissenter to this military land-grab? In "Civil Disobedience," Henry David wrote:

> If I have unjustly wrested a plank from a drowning man, I must restore it to him though I drown myself... He that would save his life, in such a case, shall lose it. This people must cease to hold slaves, and to make war on Mexico, though it cost them their existence as a people.

601p
Rain is falling ferociously today — almost like shrapnel.

29:K

Was anyone ever born in the White House? Did anyone ever die there?

211p
Just as I am obsessed with Abraham Lincoln, Grange is fixated on *Dr. De Soto* — perhaps for the same reasons. Each night, he begs me to read aloud this picture book.

30:K

The first child born in the White House was James Madison Randolph, son of Martha Jefferson Randolph, daughter of Thomas Jefferson. (Martha is now considered to have been First Lady of the United States from March

4, 1801 to March 3, 1809 because her father was a widower, making her the first First Lady who wasn't married to the president.)

Esther Cleveland, second child of President Grover Cleveland, was the second infant born in the White House, on September 9, 1893, during Cleveland's second stint as president.

Two presidents died in the White House: William Henry Harrison (1841) and Zachary Taylor (1850).

So the births and deaths are equal!

31:K

Dr. De Soto is a book by William Steig about a mouse dentist and his (nameless) loyal wife, who is also his assistant. Grange's favorite picture is a large contented cow with her eyes closed, the dental rodent standing in her mouth, focusing on one of her incisors. Grange's most beloved passage is:

> One day, when they looked out, they saw a well-dressed
> fox with a flannel bandage around his jaw.

1:L

According to Kaplan, in 1846 Lincoln attempted to become a poet. Several of his poems are extant, and they're lousy. Lincoln was wise to stick to prose, because in prose you're remembered for your best sentences, but three bad lines ruin a poem:

> Near twenty years have passed away
> Since here I bid farewell
> To woods and fields, and scenes of play,
> And playmates loved so well.
>
> The friends I left that parting day,
> Have changed, as time has sped!
> Young childhood grown, strong manhood gray,
> And half of all are dead.

But if you write enough prose you're bound to get lucky and hit on a good sentence — or a good paragraph even, which may be extracted and recited like a poem.

506p
Wait a minute, while Thomas Jefferson was a "widower" he was secretly the partner of Sally Hemings. So the third First Lady of the USA was actually a slave!

2:L

Grange isn't deeply interested in the plot of *Dr. De Soto*, about the mouse-dentist escaping a wily fox, but rather in the artwork: detailed, Germanic, melancholy. And in the rather archaic writing:

> After office hours, Mrs. De Soto molded a tooth of pure gold and polished it. "Raw with salt, indeed," muttered Dr. De Soto. "How foolish to trust a fox!"

452p
Ultimately Lincoln's most lasting achievement was his visual style. Few people can recite the Second Inaugural Address, but everyone recognizes Abe's bearded countenance on the five dollar bill, the Lincoln Memorial — and in ads for used cars on Presidents' Day! As a personality Abraham is opaque to most Americans, but as a visual icon he's intimate and beloved. Lincoln should have written: "The world will little note, nor long remember what we say here, but it will never forget how I *looked* here."

3:L

Lincoln died at the age of 56, without one gray hair.

4:L

Kaplan writes an awkward passage about Lincoln's rail-splitting:

> In the history of his family and the experience of the nation, the question of how to delineate boundaries of who owned what had had overwhelming importance. His uncle Mordecai had been killed delineating boundaries and protecting what he considered his land from Native Americans with a different definition of possession. The

corpses Lincoln had observed in the Black Hawk War had been testimony to the blood shed for territorial possession. Every acre that Thomas Lincoln farmed had previously belonged to Indian nations. Every fence that the rail-splitting youth had raised to delineate one farm from another had been an authentication of his society's commitment to the belief that a combination of physical possession and property law provided the guarantee of sure title.

I never realized that Lincoln split rails to make fences! (I thought maybe he was chopping firewood?) This does, as Kaplan suggests, argue for a unity in Lincoln's life: practicing law is the intellectual equivalent of fence-making. And the Civil War was the ultimate American dispute over fences.

6:L

Lincoln was a revolutionary! While protesting the Mexican War during his congressional term he admitted that Texans and Mexicans have a right to armed revolt:

Any people anywhere, being inclined and having the power, have the right to rise up, and shake off the existing government, and form a new one that suits them better. This is a most valuable, — a most sacred right — a right, which we hope and believe, is to liberate the world.

He sounds like Che Guevara!

7:L

Dr. De Soto ministers to a fox, though he knows the fox might eat him. He is a dentist-saint.

511p
Lincoln's stony indifference to his father has never been explained. After Abraham left his father's home in 1831, he barely saw him again. And when, in January of 1851, Lincoln heard that his 75 year old dad was on his deathbed, he wrote to John Johnston, his stepbrother:

I sincerely hope Father may yet recover his health; but at all events tell him to remember to call upon, and confide in, our great, and good, and merciful Maker; who will not turn away from him in any extremity. He notes the fall of a sparrow, and numbers the hairs of our head; and He will not forget the dying man, who puts his trust in Him. Say to him that if we could meet now, it is doubtful whether it would not be more painful than pleasant...

Perhaps Lincoln suspected — or knew — that he was illegitimate, that Thomas was not his real father. In secret, Abraham visited his true progenitor, Abraham Enloe, throughout his life. (This is just a theory.)

Lincoln's letter reminds me of Barbara Allen, in the English ballad, who coolly speaks to Sweet William as he dies of love for her:

> So slowly, slowly got she up,
> And slowly drew she nigh him,
> And the only words to him did say:
> "Young man, I think you're dying."

8:L

My new theory is that Lincoln may have enjoyed the Modern Jazz Quartet: the calm, ringing tones of Milt Jackson's vibes would have gently guided Abraham's reverie.

9:L

A mist is resting on the mountains, making them look bosomy.

10: L

Winnie left to visit her brother for a day. I'm uncomfortable without her: I fear ghosts. As I walk into the bedroom, I begin to picture Abraham Lincoln standing in the corner.

"Lincoln must be a ghost!" I realize. "He died suddenly, agonizingly, with numerous conflicts." And Lincoln would be drawn to writers who ceaselessly imagine him.

I pictured his bony hand reaching towards me.

11:L

Grange and I stopped on our walk to admire our neighbor's white mailbox. Few mailboxes are that color, which is regretful, because a white letterbox resembles a radiant Congregationalist church.

512p

Kaplan's book is repetitive and flaccid, but is (to my knowledge) the first intellectual history of Lincoln, which makes it highly useful. Lincoln was a political philosopher, in a crude, self-taught way. The crucial moment of the book occurs in January 1853, when Lincoln has finished his short career in Congress, returned to lawyering, and lost the thread of his public career. Who should visit Springfield but Ralph Waldo Emerson, delivering a lecture entitled "Power"! Here's an excerpt:

> There are men, who, by their sympathetic attractions, carry nations with them, and lead the activity of the human race. And if there be such a tie, that, wherever the mind of man goes, nature will accompany him, perhaps there are men whose magnetisms are of that force to draw material and elemental powers, and, where they appear, immense instrumentalities organize around them.

Abraham sat in the audience, quietly receptive. Emerson willed Lincoln into existence! Nine years later, Ralph Waldo visited Abraham in the White House. Immense instrumentalities had organized around him.

12:L

Winnie is not named for Winnie Mandela, of course, because they are contemporaries, but she is proud to share a hero's name. Actually, my wife was named for Winnie Winkle, a comic strip her mother loved.

13:L

Lincoln narrowly escaped being a complete loser, like his father. Or worse! If he hadn't studied law, Abraham would have labored as an itinerant rural store clerk, occasional postman, briefly a state assemblyman — too poor even to marry!

416p
On our walk, Grange and I found a blue rubber band tied into a pretzel shape. He spent 12 minutes tugging at it.

501p
Lincoln is a protean figure; he is constantly changing. I feel that every day I meet a new Lincoln.

14:L

Lincoln *is* a ghost!, I learned from the Internet. Much is known about Lincoln's ectoplasmic form. From *Ghosts in American History*:

> Grace Coolidge, wife of Calvin Coolidge, was the first person to report having seen Lincoln's apparition in the White House. She said that he stood at a window of the Oval Office, hands clasped behind his back, gazing out over the Potomac. She saw his ghost repeatedly after that.
>
> Cesar Carrera, Franklin D. Roosevelt's personal valet, ran screaming from the White House one day, after seeing Lincoln's ghost.

And those are just the first two sightings in the book!

15:L

Are there other places Lincoln's ghost haunts? His house in Springfield? His childhood home in Kentucky? Ghosts, I would imagine, move swiftly from state to state. Can they be in two places at once?

16:L

"Sometimes for three days I'll forget I'm black," Winnie said.

421p

This is like one of those trendy memoirs, such as "I spent a year living as a geisha." This is "a year of living Abrahamically."

714p

Deep inside, America wanted Lincoln's death. His motherly compassion was too noble for our mundane republic. "A nation gets the leaders it deserves" is the proverb, but for four years we possessed a leader far beyond us. Now we all feel a terrible guilt, as if we each had shot him. (This guilt manifests in that mock-Greek temple, the Lincoln Monument.)

19:L

Grange and I stood outside today gazing at a stream. It washes, washes, washes, yet the banks are never clean.

356p

In Lincoln's day, a candidate didn't have just one campaign biography. In 1860 Abraham had 18, including three in German and two in Welsh. These books were based on a narrative Abraham himself penned, in which he said of his father: "He never did more in the way of writing than to bunglingly sign his own name."

421p

The tarnish on pennies fascinates me. They are the only coins that corrode, I believe. Copper creates complex oxides: greenish, blue, white. I have a small collection of such pennies, circular grotesques (beneath which, of course, lurks the face of Abraham).

20:L

From Kaplan:

> As late as 1857, he tried and won the Effie-Afton bridge case in Chicago, a significant conflict between railroad and riverboat interests whose underlying issues fitted perfectly the mercantile and east-west transportation ideology that Lincoln and the Republican Party embraced. "There is a

travel," he told the jury, "from east to west, whose demands are not less important than that of the river. It is growing larger and larger, building up new countries with a rapidity never before seen in the history of the world."

Because Lincoln looks dowdy to us, we forget how modern he was. Today he would be proud of his iPad!

452p
John Wilkes Booth shot the president out of envy. Booth was a mediocre actor, Lincoln a great actor.

21:L

Even Lincoln's poetry improved with time. He wrote two embarrassing poems to women he met while campaigning in the late 1850s. From "To Rosa":

> You are young, and I am older;
> You are hopeful, I am not —
> Enjoy life, ere it grow colder —
> Pluck the roses ere they rot.
>
> Teach your beau to heed the lay —
> That sunshine soon is lost in shade —
> That now's as good as any day —
> To take thee, Rosa, ere she fade.

Are those sexual double entendres ("lay," "take thee") in my imagination? Maybe Lincoln *was* heterosexual.

The syntactical confusion at the end bespeaks an uncertainty in Abraham: how intimate is he with Rosa? Why doesn't he write: "To take thee, Rosa, ere *ye* fade"? Is he addressing her directly, or obliquely, in the third person? For all its flaws, however, this poem is better than Lincoln's earlier crap.

603p
Kaplan rushes through the Lincoln presidency, which is mysterious — the longer Lincoln lived, the better was his writing. My guess is that Kaplan ran out of room.

22:L

Lincoln served in the Black Hawk War for the same reason guys from Kentucky go to war today — no money! Afterwards:

> Having collected about $175 in service pay, Lincoln canoed down the Illinois River and then walked through sand ridges to New Salem.... He then purchased a share in one of the two grocery stores in New Salem. Within six months, it went bankrupt. Having purchased the share with a promissory note, he was now broke, unemployed, and in debt for a formidable amount of money: $1,100. It remained an irksome obligation for more than 10 years...

This still happens to rubes who bring home a little money from the military. If you're poor, never invest! Business is a rich man's game.

542p

I called the propane company and they put me on hold, while playing "So What" by Miles Davis. Even heard through a telephone, the song is self-levitating; John Coltrane's solo in particular. Only Miles can write a song that beatific and give it a mocking title.

602p

According to Kaplan, the South did not secede because they feared Lincoln was a radical, but because they thought him a wimp. They figured he wouldn't stop their secession. And Lincoln *was* a wimp! But in one small area, he was mighty: he insisted on preserving our republic.

The South had exercised inordinate power over the nation's politics from the beginning, when an aristocratic Virginian wrote the Declaration of Independence. In the 1850s Southerners began to feel their control wane, and panicked. (As more states entered the union, the South had less pull in Congress.) That's the main cause of the Civil War.

In a last ditch effort to solidify the South's power, the slaveholding Chief Justice of the Supreme Court, William Cheney, used the Dred Scott Decision to essentially legalize slavery in the territories. Lincoln had a keen grasp of history, and knew that this was one flaw of republics — the region with the shrewdest politicking skills dominates.

651p

The beauty of butterflies is largely a matter of scale. If they were 7 feet high, we'd shoot them.

24:L

Lincoln was a Marxist! At least when he was in Cincinnati. He gave this speech there in 1859:

> I hold that if there is any one thing that can be proved to be the will of God by external nature around us, without reference to revelation, it is the proposition that whatever any one man earns with his hands and by the sweat of his brow, he shall enjoy in peace. I say that whereas God Almighty has given every man one mouth to be fed, and one pair of hands adapted to furnish food for that mouth, if anything can be proved to be the will of Heaven, it is proved by this fact, that the mouth is to be fed by those hands, without being interfered with by any other man who has also his mouth to feed and his hands to labor with. I hold that if the Almighty had ever made a set of men that should do all the eating and none of the work, he would have made them with mouths only and no hands, and if he had ever made another class that should do all the work and none of the eating, he would have made them without any mouths and with all hands. But inasmuch as he has not chosen to make man in that way, if anything is proved, it is that those hands and mouths are to be co-operative through life and not to be interfered with. That they are to go forth and improve their condition... to the inherent right given to mankind directly by the Maker.

607p

I read Grange "The Night Before Christmas" – because it *is* the night before Christmas. We both loved it. The poem is full of elegant lines I had forgotten:

Away to the windows I flew in a flash,
Tore open the shutters and threw up the sash.

25:L

We had a small but sweet Christmas. Winnie gave me stationary with a silhouette of Lincoln in the corner. (Lincoln is slightly bent and solemn, with a snazzy top hat.) I gave her a "dream pillow" filled with rosemary, sage, chamomile. Grange received a supply of watercolors and an empty picture frame. "You can paint any picture you want, and put it in the frame," Winnie explained. "You can make a new one every day!"

26:L

Lincoln's poems are dim, but determined. Says Kaplan:

In the same letter to [Andrew] Johnston he fulfilled his promise to send a copy of a poem he admired, "Mortality," the name of whose author neither Johnston nor Lincoln knew because it had been published anonymously... When Johnston intimated that Lincoln might be its author, the latter made clear how much he aspired to write such excellent verses. "I would give all I am worth, and go in debt, to be able to write so fine a piece as I think that is."

(Lincoln was wrong. "Mortality" is doggerel, like a lot of the poetry he loved.) (Andrew Johnston was the editor of the *Quincy Whig*, a newspaper in Quincy, Illinois.)

506p
Today is entirely windless. The trees outside are as still as a mirror.

27:L

What would I say to Lincoln if I met him? It's hard to imagine actually addressing the man. In a sense we speak two separate languages. But I suppose I'd ask: "Do you regret suspending habeas corpus? Arresting thousands of citizens without warrants? Beginning the Civil War without Congress's authorization?"

I assume Abraham would offer a politician's answer, but I might see in his eyes the gleam of a tyrant.

652p

Lincoln: The Biography of a Writer completely ignores Abe's daily writings, which are often brilliant. For example:

WASHINGTON; June 13. 1862

MAJOR-GENERAL FREMONT:
Please do as I directed in the order of the 8th and my despatch of yesterday, the 12th, and neither you nor Banks will be overwhelmed by Jackson. By proper scout lookouts, and beacons of smoke by day and fires by night you can always have timely notice of the enemy's approach.
A. LINCOLN.

29:L

Grange is painting with his watercolors: dozens of little shapes that look like raindrops. (Or teardrops?)

456p

Few presidents are good writers, because a writer's mind is useless to a politician. The presidency requires decisiveness and fakery: two qualities inimical to writers. But Lincoln lived in extraordinary times, when people were desperate for clear thought. Basically, Abe became president because of his speech at Cooper Union on February 27, 1860. The intellectuals of New York City were impressed with the logic of his argument, and its beauty. (His climactic line: "Let us trust that right makes might.") Abraham contradicted their image of a provincial bumpkin, as Benjamin Franklin did for the French.

It's hard to imagine a figure like Lincoln arising today — from a windswept homestead in Wyoming, for example. The modern-day Abraham is Sarah Palin.

31:L

Twelve years ago my friend Ray and I went to Disney World and saw the Hall of Presidents. All I remember is the finale: Abraham Lincoln (the robot) standing on stage, with all the other mechanical presidents gathered beside him. In a firm but rustic voice Abraham intoned the Gettysburg Address as the sun set on a large screen behind him and stars appeared. Suddenly we recognized that the red of the sunset, the white of the clouds and the numerous twinkling stars composed an American flag!

The real Abraham had a voice quite unlike his robot's: high and reedy. In fact that's one of the reasons Lincoln became a classic writer. He *had* to compose memorable words to distract listeners from his "vocals."

549p
Grange and I found a used teabag by the road. He picked it up, and we both sniffed it. Mint! What a delighting scent to find by chance in December! Attached to the bag was a small green label: "Aromáticas Saludables."

1:A

Lincoln is beloved partly because a major poet memorialized his death. Some of the finest "slain leader" poems ever written are by Whitman:

> O powerful western fallen star!
> O shades of night — O moody, tearful night!
> O great star disappear'd — O the black murk that hides
> the star!
> [From "When Lilacs Last In The Dooryard Bloom'd."]

607p
How to account for the "madness" of Mary Todd Lincoln? Feminists suggest that she was a masterful woman who pushed her husband to be president, but afterwards had nothing left to do but shop. Or was her mistake marrying a gay man? That can be pretty stressful. (I'm sure someone has suggested this.)

2:A

My wife is out back walloping a carpet. She doesn't believe in vacuum cleaners. Instead, every few weeks she hauls one of the rugs outside, drapes it over the railing of the deck, and beats it with a baseball bat. "This rug deserves a good whacking!" Winnie likes to say.

604p
Height itself is a type of wisdom. For eight years, I faithfully listened to Howard Stern — who's even taller than Lincoln! Howard views with bemusement the foibles of his fellow creatures: their sexual cravings, resentments, political posturing. He looks at the world from above, literally. So did Abraham.
Lincoln must have been one of the tallest men in the United States!

3:A

Grange is painting again: curving snakes.

341p
We know very little about Lincoln's "depression." Basically, we know what Lincoln tells us. There's no objective medical corroboration. Friends of his describe him staring at the wall for hours, but this could be a mystical trance, not misery. They don't tell stories of Lincoln weeping.
In a work-obsessed nation like ours, any nonproductive time is considered pathology. Perhaps Lincoln himself mistook deep contemplation for "the hypo."

4:A

Abraham in Congress

Lincoln was elected to the 30th
Congress, spending two winters in the still-
new capital, a straggling, unpaved shell
of a city. A Congressman's life, with
its drudgery and details, didn't jazz

Abe. "Being elected to Congress has
not pleased me as much as I expected,"
he wrote Joshua Fry Speed. Nor did dread
overcome him on the House floor: "I was
about as badly scared, and no worse, as
I am when I speak in court." But also,
Abraham could listen. He wrote: "My old,
withered, dry eyes are full of tears yet" — when
he'd heard Alexander H. Stevens.

This is based on *Personal Traits of Abraham Lincoln* by Helen Nicolay.
The Stone Ridge Library has a first edition, from 1912. I never realized
that Joshua Speed's middle name was Fry. What a staggering three-word
name! I condensed the quote from Lincoln in lines 6 and 7; an ellipsis looks
wrong in a sonnet. The full quote — according to this book — is: "Being
elected to Congress, though I am very grateful to our friends for having
done it, has not pleased me as much as I expected."
Alexander H. Stevens later became vice president of the Confederacy!

532p
Lincoln never left the United States. In those days, you could be president
and remain entirely within our borders (especially during a civil war). The
nearest thing to a foreign nation Abe ever visited was New Orleans.

5:A

On our walk Grange found a yellow foil wrapper for Kodak film. It's
labeled "400 TX" and looks quite new, torn open near the top. I didn't know
Kodak still manufactured film.
The packaging is perfectly designed: a yellow wrapper with the simple
red word "Kodak" repeated across top and bottom. Inside, the metallic
wrapping is bright — shinier than aluminum foil. Whoever invented this
film-jacket was a minimalist master of visual rhythm.

647p
Walking with my son, I see through his small eyes. For him a
grasshopper is huge. Grange is like a living magnifying glass.

6:A

Abraham Lincoln was obsessed with a question that's still a major scholarly concern: how much did the Founding Fathers regret slavery? When Thomas Jefferson wrote in the Declaration of Independence that "all men are created equal," was he thinking of African-Americans? Lincoln studied the documents until he was sure our founding leaders were palpably ashamed of human bondage.

7:A

Lincoln and Douglas

Lincoln wanted to be Senator, more
than President — or so he told a friend,
in 1860. Stephen Douglas adored
the presidency, not the Senate. "An
ironical Fate — or our country's
beneficent Providence — gave each the
office desired by the other." In a
further twist, Douglas toured the slave states — keys
to his presidential hopes. Over and
over, he attacked Lincoln as the soul
of abolitionism. Abraham,
thus, was kept in the public mind. Straw polls
reflected this news. "People want to know
about you," Abe was told, from Chicago.

This poem is also based on the Helen Nicolay book. The first quote is from her. The second is ascribed only to "a Chicago editor," and reads in full: "You are like Byron who woke up one morning to find himself famous. People want to know about you." I'm not absolutely certain straw polls were used in 1860, though *The Dictionary of American Politics* says they began in the early 19th century. Helen capitalizes "abolitionism," but I didn't think I could get away with it.

8:A

I have no pictures of Abraham Lincoln in my house; I feel no urge to gaze at his sturdy face. For me, Abraham is an interior voice, not a visual icon.

Nonetheless, Grange saw an image of Lincoln today — as I held open a book. He stared at him closely, as if seeing his grandfather for the first time.

9:A

Did Lincoln ever attend an opera?

10:A

I sometimes imagine cheating on my wife — would it be ecstatically pleasurable, then later excruciating? Or would it seem mundane, like going bowling?

I'll never do it, I know, so it's ethical to fantasize.

444p
The Civil War reproduced Lincoln's own experience with war. His 10 weeks in the quixotic, meandering Black Hawk conflict was the pattern for the first two-thirds of the War Between the States.

516p
John Wilkes Booth and Abraham were lovers — that's the real reason for the assassination! *Sic semper tyrannis* referred to the interpersonal dynamics of their relationship, not to the nation. (Am I the first to posit this theory?)

I Googled "John Wilkes Booth and Abraham Lincoln were lovers" and found the headline "Was assassin John Wilkes Booth Abe's lover?" – in the entirely fictitious *Weekly World News* (January 22, 2002), the sidebar of the article "Abraham Lincoln Was a Woman!" (According to this theory, Booth, with his theatrical experience, helped "Lady Lincoln" disguise herself as a man.)

12:A

In the *Lincoln Reader*, I found:

"Although Lincoln never studied music, as president he probably heard more than any other occupant of the White House," wrote Douglas Jimerson. "While president he went to the theater at every possible opportunity to hear operas and musical concerts."

14:A

When I was a boy I had a bust of Lincoln, purchased for five dollars at a yard sale. It was a dramatic likeness in white plaster — though I was ashamed that this statue was actually a bank. In the back of the president's head was a slot for depositing coins. Of course, I never used Lincoln's effigy in this way. (This design was rather tasteless, given Abraham's death.) The bust presided over my bedroom for years, until, just before leaving for college, I bequeathed it to my young cousin Janon.

452p
Did Lincoln cook? For nearly four years he lived with Joshua Speed. Did Speed do all the cooking?

15:A

Winnie and Grange were drawing lines on papers today at the kitchen table. "I'll draw a wavy line," Winnie said. Grange watched her carefully. Then he drew a child's version of the same line.
"Here is a line that is smiling," Winnie said. She drew a smile-line. Grange drew his smile-line, smiling.

516p
Lincoln was one of the most tormented men in history. The only person with commensurate suffering was Jesus (who also died on Good Friday!).

16:A

Lincoln's wife is usually presented as an afterthought, almost like a pet of Lincoln's. It's true he spent a great deal of time avoiding her, but nonetheless their relationship was probably the deepest in his life. (Except maybe for Joshua Speed... Has anyone written a dual biography of Abe & Josh?)

17:A

Lincoln loved America more than any other president. His love for our nation is palpable, even a century and a half later. It was a self-destroying love.

415p
Jesus only theoretically saved people, but Lincoln actually did emancipate an entire nation of slaves. Had Abraham not lived, would slavery still exist today? A modernized slavery, where each slave has a cubicle with a computer? It's not impossible. The American South is a very traditional place.

20:A

My wife has a Greek friend who insisted that we bring $100 in cash to the local Greek Orthodox monastery. (She sent us a check for the money.) Winnie and I drove there today. The monastery is two farmhouses near Mount Tremper inhabited by two men, both in their 20s: one a monk, one a novice. Father Peter, the first one we met, was making beeswax candles, the industry of the community. He wore a black robe.
"Do you always wear robes?" I asked.
"Yes," he answered. "Black means that we are dead to the world, that we have given up our desires."
That's the color Abraham Lincoln wore!

21:A

Arthur gave me *John Wilkes Booth: A Sister's Memoir* by Asia Booth Clarke. Immediately I began to devour it. On page 50, I learned a disorienting fact: John Wilkes Booth was a cross-dresser! This scene takes place in John's youth. (Asia calls him "Wilkes.")

> Wilkes one day was lamenting his lack of grace and said that he was "jerky and stiff and too awkward for the stage." Besides, he complained; "How shall I ever have a chance on the stage? Buried here, torturing the grain out of the ground for daily bread, what chance have I of ever studying elocution or declamation?"
> He found an old book of his father's and tried to learn, from its signs, the inflection and guidance of the voice. We carefully read together Dr. Rush on the Voice, but concluded that little could be effected without a master. On several occasions he dressed himself in a petticoat and draped a

shawl around him for a toga. Then he put on my long-trained dress and walked before the long glass, declaring that he would succeed as Lady Macbeth in the sleep-walking scene. He secretly "got himself up" after Charlotte Cushman as Meg Merrilees, and terrified me and all the darkies, who shrieked, "Ondress Mars' Johnnie, ondress him!"...

I was a better judge of ease of deportment, and dressed in my skirts, with a little scarf held over his shoulders, he walked the room before the mirror, becoming more and more charmed with himself. He said merrily, "I'll walk across the field yonder, to see if the darkies can discover me."

He put on the tiny bonnet then in fashion, and went out across the fields. The men took off their hats, as they paused in their work to salute him. He passed on to the barn, where he was greeted in the same respectful manner, and came back to the house delighted with his success, which he attributed to his "elegant deportment."

Was John Wilkes Booth gay? He never married.

22:A

More from Asia's diary:

The dress of that day was considered fashionable when contrasting in colors. Wilkes wore a dark claret cloth coat with velvet lapels, a pale buff waistcoat and dove-colored trousers lightly strapped down under the boot; a broad guayaquil straw hat with a broad black ribbon band completed the costume pronounced elegant. He was always well dressed, and on this particular occasion looked remarkably handsome.

For women of that era, childhood was a golden time, before being chained to an egoistic man and constantly being pregnant. Girls could have romantic, gentle interludes with their brothers — and sisters. The high point of Asia's memoir is when she enters the forest one day with her guitar, and discovers that when she plays, frogs emerge from a pond to watch her. Later, she brings John with her, and again serenades the amphibians:

We kept silence long — or a silence only broken by the soft strumming of my guitar. Wilkes was getting impatient; but suddenly a little brown frog bounced out of the water and seated himself on a half-submerged branch of wood, then quickly came a whole congregation out of the muddy water as orderly and noiselessly as Quakers enter meeting. I played soft, now quick, now slow, and still the little ones in brown with their comical little heads and goggle eyes listened attentively.

Two young people playing a guitar in the woods — how 1960s!

As for their father, Junius Brutus, he barely appears in the memoir. He was a beloved actor who died when John Wilkes was 14. Eventually, it became clear to John that he would never achieve the status of his progenitor. John Wilkes was an immensely successful leading man, making $20,000 a year — when this was a fortune — but never entered the first rank of thespians. "Wilkes" had the rage of the epigone, the son who can't outdo his father. Only an extraordinary act, transcending mere theater, could win him lasting fame.

23:A

Similarities between John Wilkes and Abraham: both loved animals, and they read the same books! Asia describes John Wilkes' library:

A large case contained his school-books, small, cheaply-bound volumes of Bulwer, Maryatt, Byron, and a large Shakespeare, with Roman and Grecian histories, small volumes of Longfellow, Whittier, Milton, N. P. Willis, Poe, and Felicia Hemans' poems. These red-covered books had been purchased by himself or were presented by young friends.

In the 19th century, poets — especially Romantic poets — were like rock stars. Byron was equivalent to The Beatles. (One could write a PhD thesis on "Lincoln and Booth as Two Aspects of the Byronic Hero.")

"He was ardently fond of outdoor life, but was never a sportsman or an angler," Asia writes of her brother. Lincoln, too, never hunted. (I'm not sure if he fished.)

Here is one example of John Wilkes' passionate concern for natural creatures:

> He once, after nights of endeavor, caught me a katy-did just to show me what the little nuisance was like. I wanted it eagerly for my collection.
>
> "No you don't, you bloodthirsty female," he said, putting the creature in his breast. "Katy shall be free and shall sing tonight out in the sycamores." Then kissing the small thing, he said, "Oh you small devil. How you can banish sleep, quiet, and good temper! Katy, you fiend, how many nights you have kept me awake cursing your existence!" With that he walked over to the trees, and laid the little night brawler safely among the leaves, to tune her pipes for night once more.

The whole scroll of John Wilkes' inner life is written of this anecdote — a tenderness tinged with sadism, self-pity and hyper-theatricality. (Plus misogyny!)

513p
It's snowing today. Grange and I went down to watch snow fall into the stream. We learned a profound truth, but there's no word for it in English. Maybe "dissolvingness"?

541p
My intuition was right about Booth being an anarchist! Late in his life, John Wilkes tells Asia, of Lincoln: "*He* is Bonaparte in one great move, that is, by overturning this blind Republic and making himself a king. This man's re-election which will follow his success, I tell you, will be a reign!" Booth believed he was destroying a dictator.

24:A

"Wilkes" had an extreme mother complex. He was his mother's favorite, and the assassination crushed her.

What motivated Booth was guilt for not serving in the Confederate Army, plus the fear that Lincoln would make himself all-powerful. His act was purely Oedipal — kill the king (the father) and marry the mother. But in the process, he destroyed his mother, as well as the Father (Abraham) — and himself! That's the definition of neurosis (or maybe psychosis?).

Apparently, Booth was affianced at the time of his murder of Lincoln. Perhaps this was another reason for the killing? To escape matrimony?

25:A

Grange's skin is a lovely color, like ripe barley.

329p

Reading the introduction to her diary, I discovered that Asia was a poet! I wonder if her poetry exists somewhere.

353p

Lincoln's fate was inextricably tied to the lives of two short, egotistical men: Stephen Douglas and John Wilkes Booth. Douglas (the "Little Giant") foolishly responded to Lincoln's taunts, agreeing to debate him. If he hadn't, Lincoln would be unknown today. At the other end of his presidential career stands the preening John Wilkes Booth, plotting his demise. Lincoln, an honestly self-effacing man, was a magnet for diminutive egotists. (According to *Collier's Encyclopedia*, Stephen Douglas was the shortest presidential candidate in history!)

26:A

In Bob Dylan's memoir, *Chronicles: Volume One*, he sees the ghost of John Wilkes Booth:

> The room smelled of gin and tonic, wood alcohol and flowers. The place was a top floor walk-up in a Federal style building near Vestry Street below Canal and near the Hudson River. On the same block was the Bull's Head, a cellar tavern where John Wilkes Booth, the American Brutus, used to drink. I'd been in there once and saw his ghost in the mirror — an ill spirit.

Quite possibly, Lincoln and Booth are both ghosts.
Do they ever meet?

27:A

Lincoln's murder was above all else a hyper-melodrama, the gesture of an actor who could not distinguish himself from his roles. Do actors often go mad? It seems logical. Their job, after all, is to feign multiple personality disorder.

28:A

Asia's diary was published in 1938! (Before that it was too politically dangerous for the Booth family to acknowledge.) It is the key document illuminating the mind of John Wilkes Booth.

452p
Do I secretly wish I were president? No. The office would be wasted on me. I'd be a meek, forgettable Chief Executive, like Chester A. Arthur.

29:A

Winnie spoke about her father today. "He loved Israel," she remembered. "He'd say, 'It's a tiny country surrounded by enemies, but it's never afraid.'"

356p
Booth had a singular career: began as an impoverished aristocrat, became a celebrated actor, quit acting completely to speculate in oil wells, retired from oil speculation to kidnap the president, failed at kidnapping and turned to murder.
I had no idea oil wells were big money in 1864!

451p
In the photograph of Asia on the back, she is clearly a handsome woman, but there is a restraint in her face. You might even call her "clenched." And masculine. Just as, on the front cover, a femininity plays around John Wilkes Booth's features.
Asia and John were like two halves of one being, a dreamy childlike creature. They should have had BORN TO SERENADE FROGS tattooed on their arms. Both loved the gentle excesses of youth, but disliked adult

154

life. The "real world" was too prosaic for them — even the life of an actor (or the wife of an actor). John and Asia wanted every day to be Halloween.

Their childhood as rural gentry also gave them a measure of control. Their father was dead, their mother passive, their older brothers gone — and they could lord it over a little tribe of slaves. No wonder John Wilkes was wildly sentimental about "The South"!

30:A

A family almost entirely made up of actors must have been unstable. Nowadays, we picture a leading man living in a "celebrity ghetto," in California — but in the 19th century, an actor was itinerant. She (or he) was a kind of spy, even if she didn't intend to be. John Wilkes was a *real* spy, by his own admission — or boast.

31:A

Asia was pregnant with twins when John shot Lincoln. (That's one reason the Feds didn't send her to prison.) Asia had promised her brother she would name the child after him if it were a boy, but on August 20, 1865, when the infants were born, that was impossible. So she called the boy Creston Clarke. "He would grow up to become a talented and well-known actor," explains Terry Alford.

How did Asia get *her* name? Her parents were undecided "whether to call her after the accomplished young [actress] Sydney Cowell (Mrs. Bateman), who was a great favorite with Mr. and Mrs. Booth, or Ayesha, in recollection of one of Mahomet's wives." Finally, Junius wrote his wife Mary Ann: "Call the little one *Asia* in remembrance of that country where God first walked with man, and *Frigga*, because she came to us on Friday..." Thus was the child named like a complete hippie, in 1835.

542p
Grange found a dirty pen by the side of the road and asked me to read the name. It was:

uni-ball **VISION**ELITE

Now, that phrase could only have been written by a committee!

155

1:B

One of Asia's smart moves was to become a Roman Catholic within two years of the assassination. Catholicism is the religion that most dignifies suffering.

535p
History is not answers, but questions. And the most essential question is: "Does human nature exist?"

2:B

Lincoln was scared of his wife. He wasn't afraid of Robert E. Lee, but he was intimidated by Mary. For one thing, Mary was *smarter* than Robert E. Lee.

3:B

We forget how important horses were in the 1860s. They performed the work of cars and trucks. Each had a name and a distinct personality. (Yet horses are nearly absent from history books.)

503p
Would Lincoln be a popular president today? Definitely not. He would be denounced as a socialist *and* a fascist. Pundits would call him "aloof," "over-formal," "distant" — and simultaneously "clueless," "clumsy," "out of his depth."

4:B

The mystery hovering over Asia's memoir is of John Wilkes Booth's sanity. He sounds excitable — increasingly, over time — and monomaniacal. But insane? He was a well-respected actor. He invested wisely in oil. He organized a conspiracy that almost succeeded in decapitating the American government. Is this insanity?
One must admit, at the very least, he was an enterprising madman.

432p
Even if Booth and Lincoln were not lovers, they were drawn together by temperament. John was a true manic, Abraham melancholic. The manic are attracted to the depressive, while also despising them.

5:B

It's a sunny day, and on our walk Grange and I heard songbirds singing gently — almost whispering.

452p
Though the Booths grew up owning slaves in Maryland, the entire family migrated north. Apparently none had secessionist views except John. In the speech that Asia quotes in her memoir, her brother defensively praises Maryland. He says of Lincoln: "He was smuggled through Maryland to the White House. Maryland is true to the core — every mother's son. Look at the cannon on the heights of Baltimore."

John was a patriotic Southerner who wasn't really from the South. Maryland didn't secede, and in fact (according to the *Civil War Encyclopedia*) about 60,000 Marylanders fought for the Union, 25,000 for the Confederacy. The 1860 census shows essentially an equal number of free blacks and slaves!

6:B

Reading about John Wilkes Booth, I have less to contemplate than when I study Lincoln. My thought keeps going down the blind alley of the question "What is madness?"

751p
Grange and I stopped under a tree with only one leaf. Even in February, a single brown crumpled leaf still clings to this silent tree.

7:B

John Wilkes' biggest problem was that he disliked acting. He went on stage because his father had; he was successful, but never satisfied. Booth quit to speculate in oil, then quit the oil business to speculate in kidnapping. Besides being the first anarchist assassin, he was the first "performance artist." Killing a man in the balcony of a theater, while an actual play was being performed, was a gesture worthy of Artaud.

647p
Today's snow wishes it were rain. It falls slowly and sadly.

8:B

Winnie was weeping when I came home.
"What is it?" I asked.
"There are so many people who are barely surviving!" she said. "They're three days away from disaster! You could pass them on the street and never know. They all pretend to be 'middle class.' And we give them so little! It's almost a humiliation." She continued weeping.
Winnie works in the Food Stamp office.

415p
Slavery seems clearly wrong today, but this was not the case in 1860. 150 years from now, historians will look at us and ask: "How could they have allowed all their clothing to be produced in hellish factories in China? Didn't they know the workers suffered? Did they believe that Asians were subhumans — that God decreed their servitude?"

503p
Lincoln spent his life attempting to formulate a theory of human rights — one that applied to slaves, slaveowners, workers, the affluent. He never achieved an overall theory, just as Einstein never produced the Unified Field Theory.
Ironically Booth attacked Lincoln on the issue of human rights (assuming he did shout: "Sic semper tyrannus!" and not "The South is avenged!"). The most memorable line in his "To Whom It May Concern" letter — discovered by Asia in a safe in her house one April 16, 1865 — is the last line of this excerpt:

> The South *are not nor have they been fighting* for the
> continuance of slavery. The first battle of Bull-run did

158

away with that idea. Their causes *since* for *war* have been as *noble*, and *greater far, than those that urged our fathers on*. Even should we allow they were *wrong* at the beginning of this contest, *cruelty and injustice* have made the wrong become the *right*.

(Notice all the italics — like an actor making notes on a playscript, choosing which words to emphasize.) There is some truth to Booth's thesis; the American government *did* become despotic in prosecuting the war.

516p
Booth clearly descended into another reality — but whether it was espionage or madness is difficult to tell — the two being nearly identical.

531p
From *Myths after Lincoln* by Lloyd Lewis:

Edwin Forrest was the man. The tragedian was asleep in his New York hotel, the Metropolitan, on the night of April 14, 1865 when his co-star, John McCullough, came bursting into the room with the news that their friend J. Wilkes Booth had shot Abraham Lincoln.
"But I don't believe it," McCullough added.
"I do," snapped the leonine Forrest from his pillow. "All the _____ _____ Booths are crazy."

What do those two blank spaces indicate? "God damn," I assume. Though it could possibly be "shit-assed." Or "sheep-fucking." It is these ellipses that tease historians.

602p
Here in upstate New York, it's easy to get pulled back into the past. The door to the 19th century was never quite closed.

9:B

Lincoln died laughing — or rather his last conscious act was to laugh. (Booth deliberately used that laughter as a cover for his assault.)

452p

The strangest episode in John Wilkes Booth's brief life was his adventure with John Brown. Here's how Asia describes it:

> Success attended all his undertakings. He left Richmond and unsought enrolled himself as one of the party going to search for and capture John Brown. He was exposed to dangers and hardships. He was a scout, and I have been shown a picture of himself and others in their scout and sentinel dresses. He was a witness of the death of old John Brown. He acknowledged him a hero when he saw him die, and felt a throb of anguish as he beheld the old eyes straining their anxious sight for the multitude he vainly had thought would rise to rescue him.
>
> "He was a brave old man; his heart must have broken when he felt himself deserted." Uttering these words sadly, he gave me the spear of old Brown, with "Major Washington to J. Wilkes Booth" written in large letters on the handle.

John Wilkes Booth had John Brown's spear! This adamant racist was witness to the deaths of two great abolitionist heroes: Brown and Lincoln. [A footnote identifies Major Lewis Washington (1812–1871) as one of John Brown's hostages.]

516p

Booth died the same way John Brown did, surrounded by despising enemies.

601p

Grange and I discovered a red shirt hanging from a branch, in the woods. Who peeled off a shirt and draped it there? This is, in fact, a historical question.

10:B

Though Lincoln died on Good Friday, his death was more like Moses' than Jesus'. He reached the mountain overlooking the Promised Land and was forbidden by God to enter.

206p
"Where are the snakes?" Grange asked, as we strolled outside today.
"They're asleep, in the ground," I answered.
Suddenly I was conscious of walking over comatose snakes.

11:B

No one has ever made a first-rate film about the Union cause in the Civil War, but two masterpieces celebrate the South (*Birth of a Nation*, *Gone with the Wind*). Why is that? Because one theme of film is failed glory.

12:B

Yesterday it rained on the snow, and today there are millions of tiny craters. It's Nature's aerial bombardment.
Grange and I walked out, and quickly found a small, nervous mouse in the center of the road. The rodent stared at us; we returned its stare. All three of us were immobilized. Then the mouse darted to the left, reconsidered, stopped again. Again, the three-way standoff...

456p
Lincoln was the Stalin of the American Revolution. (Washington was the Lenin.) Abraham consolidated the revolution, strengthened the state and protected it from extinction. His decisions violated the spirit of the nation's founders, but also preserved their efforts — just like Stalin's.

513p
Grange and I found two Budweiser cans on the roadside, 19 feet apart. Both were tall, 24 ounce containers, with the phrase "The Great American Lager" more prominent than the usual "King of Beers."
Was some guy drinking with both hands?

14:B

The poor are often more erudite than the rich. The affluent can afford the latest mediocre novels — in hardcover! — while the poor must content themselves with Milton, Shakespeare, Cervantes. (This truth emerged in the Lincoln-Douglas debates.)

522p
What I love about Lincoln is the triumph of wisdom over cruelty. (I'm not sure that I agree with Lincoln's politics, but I admire his wisdom.) Abraham's sagacity ultimately broke the spell of slavery.

549p
On our road, my son found an envelope sent by a direct-mail solicitor. The address was:

SERVANTS OF MARY
1439 HARLEM AVE
BERWYN, IL 60402–0712

— written like that, without a period after "AVE," all capitalized. (Perhaps they were intentionally making a pun on "Ave Maria.") I wonder which of my neighbors is a secret Servant of Mary.

616p
How many countries began as colonies and became empires? The USA is almost unique. (True, France is an example, but it took them 1600 years.) We are the Cinderella of nations.

15:B

I just started *American Brutus: John Wilkes Booth and the Lincoln Conspiracies* by Michael W. Kauffman, a recent biography of Booth. The book opens with the assassination of Lincoln, and an extended death scene. Kauffman points out an obvious fact — who would go to the theater on Good Friday in 1865? Abraham died flouting God. (The closest modern equivalent would be visiting a strip club on Easter.)

523p
Without directly mentioning it, *American Brutus* shrewdly draws parallels between Lincoln's assassination and September 11. (The book was published in 2004.) For hours and days after Lincoln's death, no one knew the extent of the uprising. Would Washington burn? Would the last Southern soldiers burst into the city and take control? (It might have been

162

possible, in the confusion.) Rumors flew. Seward was dead! The assassin had been caught! It was like the chaos on September 11, 2001. The World Trade Center had been hit – twice! The Pentagon was attacked! Would the government fall?

604p
Today's road find: a black plastic bowl, labeled "Burger King", and spattered with ketchup and grease. How grotesque are the remains of our Whoppers!

16:B

I notice that I am raising my child the same way Lincoln raised his kids, with indulgence and delight. I hope Grange turns out better than Lincoln's luckless boys.

617p
From *American Brutus*:

The following day, the careworn president renewed his oath of office in the old Senate chamber. After the ceremony, Lincoln walked to the capital's east front to address the public. As he stood up to speak, the sun broke through the clouds and bathed him in a ray of bright light. He then began what many consider to be his finest speech, full of hope and promise for a reunited nation.

"With malice toward none; with charity for all; with firmness in the right, as God gives us to see the right, let us strive on to finish the work..."

Many people were surprised that Lincoln had made it this far. He had beaten the odds, and he stood there now, in his moment of glory, to set a brighter tone for the nature's future. Little did he suspect that in six weeks he would die at the hands of a man he would have recognized — and who was even then standing just a few feet away.

The truth is that celebrity culture has not changed much since Lincoln's day. If Tom Cruise wanted to kill Obama, he undoubtedly could.

17:B

Grange found a Milky Way wrapper on the road — brown and generic. (Didn't the wrapping once bear an image of the actual Milky Way?)

458p
When Abraham arrived for his first inauguration, by train, it was rumored that he'd disguised himself as a Scotsman to travel through Maryland without being detected. (Maryland was rife with rebellion.) Images of President Lincoln in a Tam o' Shanter were widely circulated. This absurd image — though untrue — weakened Abraham's presidency.

18:B

American Brutus describes how the veneration of Lincoln began at the moment of his death. Clearly, the Abraham we have today is the creation of John Wilkes Booth.

19:B

Booth *lost money* on his oil speculation:

> Booth never saw a penny from his investments. The Dramatic Oil well, nicknamed "the Wilhelmina," pumped hardly more than a trickle, and the driller's attempt to blast it did more harm than good. In all, the venture cost Booth six thousand dollars and depleted much of his savings.

But John Wilkes lied about his oil ventures to Asia, and she believed him. (Also, he lied about them to everyone.) Though "Dramatic Oil" is a fabulous name for a corporation!

414p
The Booth conspirator I identify with is the loutish, greedy George Atzerodt. He was always getting drunk and boasting about his upcoming triumphs, as when he told a stableman the night of the assassination: "You will soon hear of a present" – an awful, twisted phrase. Then when the moment arrived for him to assassinate Andrew Johnson, he wandered around uselessly.

Writes Kauffman:

> ... even soaked in alcohol, his mind could see the trap he
> had fallen into. He was not a killer, and he had no intention
> of becoming one. But by now he was in too deeply, and
> there was nothing he could do. (He voiced his objections,
> but Booth shrugged them off. "Then we will do it," he said.)

Reading this suspenseful story, I'm rooting for Atzerodt to escape the
police, though I know he won't. In the photograph at the center of the
book, Atzerodt looks dejected, remorseful, but poetic — not unlike
Baudelaire (his contemporary). Why do I see myself in the face of this
greasy creep?

459p
Atzerodt was a German, born in Thurlingen! Only in America can you
arrive on a boat, become a carriage repairman, and within six years be hung
as an assassin!

20:B

The crows are not speaking today. It's a day of consensual crow silence.

402p
Kauffman writes:

> Wednesday, April 19, began with the firing of guns. This
> was a national day of mourning, and hourly tributes were
> sounded in every place an artillery unit could be found. A
> funeral service would take place in the White House,
> followed by a trip to the Capitol, where the president's
> remains would lie on public display... Window shades
> were drawn in the Executive Mansion, and the gaslight
> was dimmed.

I never knew the White House had gaslight in Lincoln's day.

21:B

Winnie, Grange and I went for a walk together. We came to a stream and heard a large flapping sound. To our right, a bald eagle flew up from a bush. He rose into the air, crossed the stream, then settled onto the branch of a tree, looking majestic and narcissistic.

I knew bald eagles lived in Stone Ridge, but I'd never seen one.

203p

American Brutus begins with a minute-by-minute description of the Friday Abraham was killed, including a long description of the death watch. Lincoln had a great body! Though it had been years since he'd done physical labor, he was still a powerful man:

> [Dr.] Leale carefully removed the president's garments and tossed them, with the half-Wellington boots, off to the side. He was surprised to see what a remarkably strong physique Mr. Lincoln had. At fifty-six, he still had the chest and arms of an athlete. The doctors marveled at his muscular development, and one observer noted that if Lincoln were not possessed of such vital power, he would have died within ten minutes of being shot.

Both Booth and Abraham died prolonged deaths — though Abraham's was apparently rather peaceful, and John Wilkes' excruciating.

439p

John Wilkes Booth's act may be seen as an attack on theatre itself — soiling the sacred sanctuary of a playhouse.

456p

The weathered wood of clothespins is one of the loveliest sights on earth.

22:B

If songbirds are descended from dinosaurs, does this mean that dinosaurs sang?

601p
Like many fine books, *American Brutus* makes its case in the title. Kauffman does not see John Wilkes as mad, wildly envious of his brothers, seeking eternal fame — but as a true revolutionary, attacking tyranny. And he makes the case, to his credit, for Abraham-as-dictator, especially in Maryland, which was governed by martial law for much of the war. Yes, Booth was melodramatic, grandiloquent, and pretty fanciful — he planned to kidnap Lincoln at Ford's Theatre in full view of a thousand people — but that's not exactly madness.

23:B

If I say, "I'm writing about Washington," it can mean a dozen things — the nation's capital, the state, etc. — but "I'm writing about Lincoln" only has one meaning. (A historian specializing in Lincoln, Nebraska wouldn't use that phrase.) Lincoln is the more indelible figure, actually one of the few presidents you can picture in your mind. (Try to summon up an image of Grover Cleveland.)

536p
I am writing this book, in part, to free Lincoln's ghost. Walk off, Abraham! Move forward! Henceforth, you need not preside over our nation. Somehow we'll soldier on without you!

24:B

At the Stone Ridge Library Fair I found the book *Knowledge in a Nutshell* by Charles Reichbloom. It has astonishing stories in it, supposedly true. This is from Chapter 4, "U.S. History":

> Who would have predicted success for this man?
> First, he failed in business. Then, he tried politics.
> He ran for his state legislature — and lost.
> Then, he ran for the U.S. House of Representatives — and lost.
> Then he ran for the U.S. Senate — and lost. He ran for the U.S. Senate again — and again lost.

He was nominated for U.S. Vice President, and lost.
Then, he ran for President of the United States — and
won. His name: Abraham Lincoln.

It's all true — I think — but omits the elections he won: four for the
Illinois House of Representatives, one for Congress.

541p
If forced to define jazz, I would call it "sexy prayer."

25:B

The Civil War was the American epic — our *Mahabharata*, our *Iliad*.
(Too bad it was never memorialized in verse. Instead, our literary epic is
about killing whales.)

26:B
A great historian is always a great gossip.

403p
All the classic jazz albums have beautiful names: *Birth of the Cool*, *A Love
Supreme*, *The Shape of Jazz to Come*. Even the album I'm listening to now,
What Is There to Say? by Gerry Mulligan and Art Farmer, has a deceptively
simple, yet perfect title — suggesting that all music is conversation.

517p
My wife has a habit of shaking her head from side to side, as if
thinking: "This looks bad! This looks real bad!" When I ask about this
habit, she denies it: "I'm not shaking my head!"

1:C

Grange and I found a large can of Heineken today:

BREWED WITH
PASSION FOR QUALITY

He was mesmerized by the red star, and ran his finger over and over it.

451p
If the Civil War were a prizefight, it would be as dramatic as *Rocky*. In the first round, the North was pummeled. In the second, third, fourth and fifth rounds, he spun around confusedly. In the ninth round, he began his comeback — with a "War is hell!" cry. By the last round, the Union had utterly decimated his opponent.

459p
The failures of his father compelled Abraham to become a father himself, for the entire nation. But his "fatherhood" was a failure. Half his "children" hated him; one killed him. Lincoln's fathership was accepted only by posterity, and Walt Whitman.

3:C

Did Abraham have a middle name?

5:C

Abraham designed himself. After years of contemplating pictures of George Washington, he chose the physical adornments that would transform him into an icon: beard, black clothes, stovepipe hat, occasional shawl. (Abe assessed his own physical features, and found the complementary shadings he needed.) Being a lover of progress, he wisely seized on photography as his medium. Abe's photos are the best of any president's, except possibly John F. Kennedy's.

605p
Do all extremely tall people feel that they have been chosen for a singular destiny? (I guess I mean men; it's hard to think of prominent tall women.)

7:C

I picked up *Our Lincoln* again, the Eric Foner anthology I read last year. Paging through the Harold Holzer essay, I noticed:

> Two years later the family greeted the birth of Thomas Lincoln, Abraham's father's namesake, who was nicknamed Tad by his father.

169

So Abraham didn't totally hate his father! He named his fourth son for him. (Tad died of heart failure at the age of 18, in 1871.)

604p
The death of Abraham was the first national day of mourning in American history. Abraham taught our young nation collective grief.

8:C

Fake-looking snow is falling. If I saw this snow in a movie, I'd think, "The prop department is out of money. Those are soap flakes!"

456p
When I was a kid you still heard the phrase "Honest Abe" — but it has vanished. Honesty is a discarded American virtue.

9:C

Did Abraham's father beat him — I mean, more brutally than most fathers slapped their sons? Is that why Abe never visited him?

507p
Abraham had no middle name.

11:C

How does my wife compare to Mary Todd Lincoln? She dominates me, certainly, but from a quiet authority, not with tantrums.

604p
Thanksgiving exists due to Abraham. In a free newspaper called *The Lincoln Eagle* (the edition XXXII October/November 2011) I learned this, in an article entitled simply "Did You Know?":

> Proclamation of Thanksgiving, Washington DC-October 3, 1863
> This is the proclamation which set the precedent for America's national day of Thanksgiving. During his

administration, President Lincoln issued many orders like this. For example, on November 28, 1861, he ordered government departments closed for a local day of thanksgiving.

The holiday we know today as Thanksgiving was recommended to Lincoln by Sarah Josepha Hale, a prominent magazine editor. Her letters to Lincoln urged him to have the "day of our annual Thanksgiving made a National and fixed Union festival." The document below sets apart the last Thursday of November at "as a day of Thanksgiving and Praise."

(The rest of the article consists of the proclamation.) The one American holiday free of shopping and hysteria — naturally it was Lincoln's.

617p
And as for Sarah Josepha Hale, she wrote the nursery rhyme "Mary Had a Little Lamb"!

12:C

Did Whitman compose heartfelt paens to Lincoln because he *sensed* Abraham was gay? (Or knew he was, through the queer grapevine?)

456p
In order to be an icon, one must practice visual consistency. If you wear a different outfit every day, you can't become symbolic.

13:C

Thomas Edison (1847–1931) only had three months of education. Perhaps every great American never went to school. Are there any such Europeans, or did America create the uneducated hero?

416p
Abraham's stepmother survived him — like Jesus's mother! (She died four years later.) But when did Mary die?

604p
Hyppolitus of Thebes states that Mary outlived Jesus by 11 years, dying in the year 41.

607p
In a sense, Abraham's dream languished for 100 years, until Martin Luther King stood before his memorial to declare:

> Five score years ago, a great American, in whose symbolic shadow we stand today, signed the Emancipation Proclamation. This momentous decree came as a great beacon light of hope to millions of Negro slaves who had been seared in the flames of withering injustice. It came as a joyous daybreak to end the long night of their captivity.

14:C

The word that comes to mind for Winnie is "soothing."

601p
A book on Abraham must decide where to begin — at his birth? The moment after his death? His first day as president? I would start my biography at the end of Abe's luckless service in the Black Hawk War, when his horse died and he began his long trek back to Salem. We are all the same in success, but each person is unique in adversity. At this utterly dispossessed moment, Abraham was quietly stoic.

16:C

Grange and I went outside and tasted snowflakes in our mouths — much easier than catching a falling leaf!

607p
I'm reading a children's book called ... *If You Grew Up With Abraham Lincoln* by Ann McGovern. Here's an excerpt:

> When Lincoln was postmaster of New Salem, he carried letters in his hat. And when he was a lawyer in Springfield,

he carried papers in his hat. Into his hat went newspaper
clippings and notes he wanted to remember.

How pleasant to contemplate the capacious hat of Abraham Lincoln!
It would make a good book: *The Secrets of Lincoln's Hat*.

17:C

Springfield Fashions

Women in Springfield read *Godey's Lady
Book* to learn the latest fashions from New
York and Paris, then copied a few
of the patterns, to produce bright, weighty
dresses of their own, to wear proudly at
the next cotillion or dance. The sleeves were
wide, the waists narrow, the fabric silk or
velvet or satin, with sub-layers that
rustled. Stolen fashions were no stigma;
rather a sign of high style. A lace veil
nicely complemented a gown — or a pale
pink fan — adding an air of enigma
to a Springfield damsel, whose glances
might provoke a young lawyer's advances.

All the information is taken from ... *If You Grew Up With Abraham
Lincoln* — in fact, all from one page. The word "bright" was not in the
text; I inferred that from the illustration. (The "young lawyer" in the last
line is Abraham.)

18:C

Trees are not stationary; they move. Humans use nerve impulses to
motivate their limbs; trees use wind, bird-hopping, and squirrel-climbing.

451p
Is it possible that homosexuality was entirely accepted on the American
frontier, and that the contemporary horror of it is recent — resulting from
later developments in Christianity?

.

505p
The sky is as clean as shampoo'd hair.

20:C

Abraham would be considered a pacifist today. He vigorously opposed the Mexican War, and was quite sarcastic about the one war in which he fought. The reason he prosecuted the Civil War is that he believed the South had no right to secede. For Abraham, this was a purely legal matter. If the Constitution had read: "Every state has the power of secession," we'd be two nations today.

504p
Marriage is a study in self-love. The central question is: "Do I deserve affection?"

703p
I'm reading Garry Wills' *Lincoln at Gettysburg: The Words That Remade America*. On page 75 Wills reveals that Lincoln's depression made him popular! He quotes Herndon on Abraham: "His apparent gloom impressed his friends, and created sympathy for him — one means of his great success." In the Romantic era, explains Wills, melancholy was cool. Lincoln was like Bob Dylan during *Blonde on Blonde*: remote, lanky, engagingly tortured.

21:C

The bears are not yet awake, but they're beginning to yawn.

22:C

Lincoln was the first beatnik president. Why? 1) He dressed in black. 2) He had a fringe beard. 4) He wrote poetry.

515p
Wills quotes the famous racist speech of Lincoln's from Charleston, Illinois:

... And I will say, in addition to this, that there is a physical difference between the white and black races which I believe will for ever forbid the two races living together on terms of political and social equality. And inasmuch as they cannot so live, while they do remain together there must be the position of superior and inferior, and I as much as any other man am in favor of having the superior position assigned to the white race.

Even at his most racist, Lincoln is perfectly willing to consider the possibility of African-Americans as masters and whites as slaves.

23:C

I found Knighty under the armchair in the living room. Grange had cast him aside, heedlessly.

703p
Abraham was a psychological figure. Looking into the eyes of his portraits one sees complexity, as one doesn't in George Washington's. Our Founding Fathers had the maturity of 10 year olds.

24:C

Before giving his speech at Gettysburg, Wills notes that "Lincoln sat his horse gracefully (to the surprise of some)." I have seen pictures of Lincoln on horseback, and they do look wrong — as if the horse should be riding on him?

509p
My life has moved in the opposite direction of Lincoln's, from city to forest. I am living Lincoln's life backwards.

514p
Garry Wills agrees with me that Lee was an idiot at the battle of Gettysburg — and says so in the first line of his Prologue:

Not all the gallantry of General Lee can redeem, quite, his foolhardiness at Gettysburg.

26:C

Even if Lincoln wasn't gay — if he only slept (platonically) with a man for 3 3/4 years, whom he deeply loved — that's pretty close!

351p
Winnie told me that songbirds wake up early, sing for a couple hours, then go back to sleep. What a surprise! The proverb should be amended: "The early bird catches the worm — then takes a nap."

27:C

Arthur gave me the "What Would Lincoln Do?" issue of *Time* (Vol. 180, No. 19, November 5, 2010). In one essay Doris Kearns Goodwin remarks that Lincoln laughed at his own jokes:

> His "eyes would sparkle with fun," one old-timer remembered, "and when he had reached the point in his narrative which invariably evoked the laughter of the crowd, nobody's enjoyment was greater than his."

Some joke-tellers ruin everything by laughing, but Abraham was a rare man whose laughter itself was funny.

29:C

Winnie and I sat listening to Dinah Washington on a CD this evening:

> This bitter earth,
> What a fruit it bears!
>
> What good is love
> That no one shares?

We held hands.

452p

I wish I knew what Abraham ate — not when he was young and had no choice, but when he was older and could decide. What were his favorite dishes? Pork sausage? Roast turkey? I can't even imagine.

503p

Each decade has its own Abraham. Americans interpret Lincoln's life according to their needs: sometimes he's a superhuman demigod, sometimes an activist, or a smug racist. I found *Abraham Lincoln* by Ingri and Edgar Parin D'Aulaire, a children's book from 1957 ("a completely redrawn and amplified new edition" of a book from 1939) in the High Falls Library. In it Abraham is a proletarian Everyman, with the virtues of the working class: humor, selflessness, quick thinking, occasional laziness. A representative passage gives the fullest account I have yet read of the Black Hawk War:

> ... the men of New Salem were called to war, for an Indian chief, Black Hawk, had come back to Illinois with his warriors. His tribe had sold the land to the "paleface," but Black Hawk said: "Man-ee-do, the great spirit, gave us the land, it couldn't be sold." "Sold is sold," said the people of Illinois, and went to war to chase the Indians out.
>
> Abe Lincoln went to war as a captain. The man from each village who had the longest row of men lined up behind him was elected captain. And twice as many men lined up behind Abe as behind his rival. But his soldiers had never taken orders from any man before, and Captain Abe Lincoln struggled hard to make them obey him. That was all the fighting he had. For Black Hawk and his warriors fled before the soldiers. One day a peaceful Indian came walking into Camp. The soldiers were angry and wanted to kill him, but Abe said, "Anyone who touches him must fight me first." Because he was the strongest, they had to obey.
>
> Soon after that Black Hawk was taken prisoner, and The Indian War was over.

514p
Grange and I stood outside today, listening to the East Wind bullying the sky.

30:C

According to Ingri and Edgar Parin D'Aulaire, Abraham was perfectly cheerful until he fell in love:

> His friends believed in him, and most of all a girl, whose name was Ann Rutledge. She was sure he would become a great man some day, if he would just go on with his studies. And then they would be married, and be happy ever after.
>
> But one day Ann Rutledge took sick and nothing could be done to save her life. From that day on it was as if there were two Abes. The one was gay and full of funny stories, the other was so sad and sorrowful that no one dared to approach him.

Let me point out that according to the book jacket, "The D'Aulaires have read everything they could find about Lincoln's life, his sayings and his ways, and also about the period in which he lived."

459p
Abraham started school when he was six! That's pretty early for frontier life — one reason he became truly literate.

503p
The clear declarative sentences of a children's book are best for evoking Abraham's life. Like all saints, his ultimate virtue was simplicity.

603p
Today's is a deep rain — a rain extending for miles.

31:C

I found a copy of *A Comprehensive Anthology of American Poetry* the library was throwing out, containing Vachel Lindsay's poem about Abraham:

178

Abraham Lincoln Walks at Midnight
(In Springfield, Illinois)

It is portentous, and a thing of state
That here at midnight, in our little town
A mourning figure walks, and will not rest,
Near the old court-house pacing up and down.

Or by his homestead, or in shadowed yards
He lingers where his children used to play,
Or through the market, on the well-worn stones
He stalks until the dawn-stars burn away.

A bronzed, lank man! His suit of ancient black,
A famous high top-hat and plain worn shawl
Make him the quaint great figure that men love,
The prairie-lawyer, master of us all.

He cannot sleep upon his hillside now.
He is among us:—as in times before!
And we who toss and lie awake for long
Breathe deep, and start, to see him pass the door.

His head is bowed. He thinks on men and kings.
Yea, when the sick world cries, how can he sleep?
Too many peasants fight, they know not why,
Too many homesteads in black terror weep.

The sins of all the war-lords burn his heart.
He sees the dreadnaughts scouring every main.
He carries on his shawl-wrapped shoulders now
The bitterness, the folly and the pain.

He cannot rest until a spirit-dawn
Shall come;—the shining hope of Europe free;
The league of sober folk, the Workers' Earth,
Bringing long peace to Cornland, Alp and Sea.

It breaks his heart that kings must murder still,
That all his hours of travail here for men
Seem yet in vain. And who will bring white peace
That he may sleep upon his hill again?

It's my favorite Lincoln poem. (Lindsay was born in Springfield, in a house where Abraham's sister-in-law once dwelled.)

1:D

Abraham Lincoln (the children's book) makes an obvious point that I had never considered: the Gettysburg Address is the most melancholy great speech ever given. It is, ultimately, a dialogue between Abraham and his "hypo":

> But in a larger sense, we cannot dedicate, we cannot consecrate, we cannot hallow this ground. The brave men, living and dead who struggled here have consecrated it far above our poor power to add or detract. The world will little note nor long remember what we say here...

705p
Ingri and Edgar Parin D'Aulaire's *Abraham Lincoln* ends with our hero still alive — just five days before his death! This book is a radical revision in which Abraham never dies:

> The Civil War had come to an end. The slaves were free, and the Union was saved. Most people in the Northern States wanted to make the Southerners pay for the four terrible years of war. But Lincoln said they should be received back into the Union "with malice toward none, with charity to all." He felt like the father of a great flock of children. Some had run away, but were now returning to their home. He stood on a balcony at the White House, looking out over the cheering people who cried: "Speak, Father Abraham." Abraham Lincoln didn't answer with words. But he made the band play "Dixie," the favorite song of the Southerners, which had not been heard in Washington since the Civil War began. Then he sat down

on his rocking chair to rest. He had done what he should
do. He had held together the great nation brought forth
upon this continent by his forefathers.

I love the Abraham Lincoln of 1950s children's books, the one who
may be addressed without irony as "Father Abraham."

The End